TO
FARM
IS TO
LIVE

An autobiographical account
of farming in the
East Riding of Yorkshire
from the 1920s to the 1990s

NORMAN E. KIRKWOOD

FIRST PUBLISHED 1999
© The Kirkwood Family

Cover illustration from an
original watercolour painting by
Chris Atkinson: *'Harvest at Elmswell Wold'*.

Photograph of Norman Kirkwood on the
introductory page is by courtesy of
Farmers' Weekly Picture Library.

ISBN 0-901934-32-1

Designed and produced for the
Kirkwood Family by
THE RIDINGS PUBLISHING CO. LTD.
33 Beverley Road, Driffield,
East Yorkshire YO25 6SD.

Printed and bound by
Redwood Books, Trowbridge, Wiltshire.

Foreword

I FIRST met Norman Kirkwood in the 1970s when he welcomed me into the local Lions Club; a ruddy-faced man with a strong handshake, a warm smile and a boyish curl above a furrowed brow.

Our paths have not crossed often in recent years apart from the occasional meeting in the street; but, having been privileged to edit and see through this book to completion, I now wish I had come to know him better.

I can truly say that I have learned more about farming — the way things are and, more particularly, were — through the pages of this autobiography than I have picked up in nearly 40 years of living at the centre of this farming area.

This book is a delicious piece of social history. Those in the farming community who knew Norman will identify so clearly with what he has set down. Others, like me, who live here but are apart from it, will wish they too had come to know him. His simple philosophies (and those passed down from his father) . . . his shrewdness in business . . . his love of the land . . . shine through in a most delightful and thoroughly readable way.

It has been a real pleasure to have been involved with the family in seeing Norman's labour of love come to fruition . . . from hand-written pages on a note pad to . . . a book you will enjoy.

Winston Halstead,
Editor, *Yorkshire Ridings Magazine*,
Driffield, East Yorkshire.

NORMAN KIRKWOOD was born into a farming family in the late 1920s. In those days it was usual for a farmer's son to follow in his father's footsteps and Norman was no exception to that rule.

Married in his early twenties he became a devoted family man and a rock to those close to him. As his life progressed so did farming and Norman made it his business to progress with it. A motto he often quoted was: 'Live as though you are going to die tomorrow and farm as if you are going to live forever' . . . and he did just that!

If one is lucky, retirement comes inevitably. Norman looked back on his life (three years ago) and realised the changes he had seen. He decided to make a record for the family as he concluded that no other generation would see as many changes in their lives as he had. His dreams and ambitions have been recorded in this life story and, as a tribute to him, the family felt it their duty to fulfil his last ambition which was to publish this book.

Norman Eric Kirkwood died on the 22nd February, 1999.

Chapter One

I WAS born in Skirlaugh, a small village in the East Riding of Yorkshire, in 1927, in the midst of probably the worst agricultural recession Britain has ever experienced. If the young farmer of today considered he was having a rough ride during 1997 and 1998, compared to his forefathers who farmed through the Twenties and Thirties, he ain't seen nothing yet!

I was the fourth child of a family of six, two girls and four boys. The whole family became involved in farming in later life; the girls both married farmers and the boys all took up farming in their own right. I have lived on five farms in my life, and have farmed in Holderness, on the Yorkshire Wolds and in the North Riding of Yorkshire.

I have been involved in four partnerships which gave me an insight into the advantages and disadvantages of the system. Two of these partnerships were in farming and two non-farming enterprises. I have always maintained that a partnership should not exceed twenty years, as if it has not achieved what it was set out to do in that time it never will.

A successful partnership is like a good marriage: it enables two people to do what they could not have done without the other, albeit with a certain amount of risk. Also, the two people who form it should preferably be the ones to dissolve it, as, if it drags on into the next generation, it is a recipe for disaster.

The one big disadvantage of a partnership, is that each partner is

1

responsible for the other's debts, hence the saying 'the only ship you should not join is a partnership.'

The 1920s fell between two World Wars and were probably some of the worst farming years anyone in that era had ever seen. During this period there were no advances in technology either. Landlords were desperately looking for tenants to take over the land which they, themselves, had farmed through the prosperous years of the First World War and before. In order to attract a tenant the rents were very low and sometimes a rent-free start-up period was agreed.

When the Second World War broke out in 1939, not only had agriculture been stagnant all those years, but also manufacturing industries were in no better shape either, which made the outlook for this country very bleak. Farmers were therefore encouraged to set their wheels in motion, as it was realised that the ships loaded with grain, fruit and many other food products, would not be delivering to our ports again for the duration of the war. So farming, once again, became a very important industry.

My father started farming in 1921 when he took the tenancy of Poplar Farm in the village of Skirlaugh, which was a mixed holding of 120 acres of heavy clay land, typical of the Holderness area. The capital needed to take such a farm in those days was ten pounds an acre: this covered all costs or, as they would have said, 'lock stock and barrel'.

My father had never received any wages, which was normal in those days. He did, however, get a small amount of pocket money and his keep, which was called 'meat for work'. This meant that when he started in business, backed by his father, he had to borrow money from the bank.

The very next year, 1922, the farming community woke up to a financial collapse; the valuation on all farms had been reduced by half overnight. Horses which father had bought for £70 were worth £35 and they were the most expensive item on the farm.

Not only had his assets dropped by half: this was borrowed money, so there was a dramatic increase in his bank charges and he never made a profit until 1937. This was fifteen years of a young man's working life gone, the years we now expect to lay the foundation of a good family business.

The depression of the 1920s put many farmers into liquidation: some of the very rich were unable to tighten their belts and reduce their standard of living, and most of the ones on borrowed money did not survive. In fact, father always said that those who borrowed money to buy land after the First World War went bust, and he never forgot it.

He would often say to us as lads: "Never forget as you climb the ladder in this life, if you ever come down it you will be meeting the same folk." In other words, "Do as you would be done by."

He once told the tale of a neighbouring farmer going bankrupt, a very good and hard working man. He paid nineteen and sixpence in the pound, and the bank broke him for sixpence short in the pound. He advised us to never borrow money to buy land: "As the banks would lend you an umbrella when the sun was shining, but would take it away when it started to rain."

I say to this day that my father only ever gave me one piece of bad advice and that was not to borrow money. As I see it, if you haven't got any money and you don't borrow some, you have no chance of starting a business. If you borrow money at 7% and make 15% out of that money, then that is good business.

Father also told the tale of a wealthy farmer riding to the hounds in pink coat and top hat, who rode past him one day whilst he was busy cleaning out a roadside dyke. The huntsman said: "Good morning, Kirkwood." Father replied: "Good morning." Two years later the same gentleman walked into my father's stackyard to carry chaff from the threshing machine; this was the rock bottom job on the farm and there was no chance of him ever getting back into farming.

In 1927 we saw the wettest Bank Holiday for many years. Petrol that year at 1s.-1d. a gallon, was at its cheapest since 1902. New regulations were introduced to limit the length of a car to 27 feet 6 inches. Also that year, to buy a seven-bedroomed house in Holland Park, London, would have cost £1,750.

In 1928, although farming was still very tough, father decided to look for a larger farm. As the saying goes: 'When the going gets tough the tough get going'. He was offered any one of 100 farms that the agent had on his books to let. He looked round Manor Farm, Dunnington; this was a 320-acre farm, which was in very poor condition. The heavy land was run down and covered with wicks and all manner of weeds, and the farm needed a lot of attention to the dykes and drainage.

The landlord, Squire Robert Dixon, offered my father the first two years rent-free, in order to persuade him to take on the farm. This was the only way in those days to actually attract a tenant, and the only way a tenant without capital could expand. Today farming is big business; then it was only a way of life.

April 6th, 1928, was moving day. All farms changing hands did so on the 6th of April each year; it was known as 'Lady Day'. To my way of thinking it was anything but a Ladies' Day! Imagine having to do the move along with four children aged five, four, three and yours truly eight months old and, on top of that, another one due the following August . . . and then they ask: "What did they do for leisure in those days?" The only transport available was horses and wagons.

Father and mother were up at the crack of dawn loading their furniture and household goods safely on the wagon, for the nine-mile journey to their new home. It was all action there as well, as the previous occupiers vacated the house and farm.

I said 'new home': this consisted of the lavatory at the bottom of the garden, the water supply from the pump near the garden gate, the paraffin lamp and candle sticks for the lights. There was hot water in a boiler next to the kitchen fire, providing that the fire was lit, or else it was cold. A copper in the outside wash-house provided water both to wash all the clothes at four o'clock on Monday morning and also, hot water for the weekly bath night on Friday. With all these basic facilities in mind, I suppose that I should have said 'another home'.

So, when mother and father arrived at their new home with all their goods and shackles, the first thing to do was put the fireside rug down and place me, the eight-month-old baby boy, on to it for the next three hours. I don't remember it boring me one bit. After that the rest of the furniture and carpets were put in some sort of order in their new home; surely the only piece of furniture of any concern to my mother by this time must have been the bed. So there it was, I had arrived at the second farm of my life!

Apart from moving home, all farm machinery and livestock had to be moved as well. Neighbouring farmers always helped with the 'flitting' and also gave the new tenant a day's ploughing at a later date, even though they were unlikely to know him.

The village of Dunnington consisted of six farms, six farm cottages, a church and a chapel which we visited on a weekly basis. There was also, of course, 'The Manor House' where Squire Dixon lived. He had lost his wife and lived with his daughter who was a spinster. He employed two housemaids, a cook, two gardeners and a chauffeur. The large house stood in five acres of land and the gardens were extensive.

The Squire was an eccentric character and, as a young boy, I can remember him calling me any name that came into his head; his favourite was Bob, but he never gave you your proper name. He would offer you a thrupenny bit to sing him a song, and would sit with a broad grin on his face enjoying every moment of it. Sometimes when he was walking round the farm he would say to one of father's staff: "If you finish that job, Bob, before tonight I'll give you half a crown," and, true to his word, he did.

5

He had a word for everyone, no matter what their status was and could always tell an interesting tale. He once told my father about how in the 1880s they drained a field called Slack on the farm. In order to get the water into the main dyke, an outfall had to be dug by hand, through a clay hill to the depth of 16 ft. All the doors were taken off the farm buildings to use as shuttering, to prevent the sides from caving in, as it would not have been safe to do the work without.

The digging was done by a step system with men standing at different levels. They rotated jobs throughout the day. Each man had a turn digging, as this was the hardest work, while the rest of the force shovelled the loose soil to the surface. It is interesting to note that the outfall drained that field for over a hundred years.

Squire Dixon was born in August, 1852, and died in October, 1932, at the age of 80. It is nearly 150 years since his birth and I still remember being in the meadow field and seeing the funeral procession leaving the Manor, on the three-mile journey to Beeford Parish Church, where the service was held. I was five years old at the time, and to the villagers of Dunnington, it was as if they had lost a king.

Dunnington was well served with trades' people, most of whom lived in local villages within a three-mile radius.

Miller Tom travelled from Beeford in his horse and trap; he supplied the housewives with their flour and the farmers with their cattle food requirements.

For protein there was the choice of linseed or cotton cake. This came in slabs, which were two feet long, one foot wide and one inch thick. These had to go through a hand-turned machine called a cake crusher, and that's exactly what it did, making them into small pieces the cattle could eat. These were then mixed with rolled oats to make a balanced ration, or as near as possible, on the day.

Miller Tom also supplied rolled oats, but in most cases the farmer would take his own oats to the mill and have them rolled by contract; this was quite a large part of Tom's business. After two years the farmers would get a bill for this and even then if they were unable to settle in full, part payment would be accepted. The house-wife would pay her flour bill when she was able, but he never put pressure on anyone, and you did not take people to court for non-payment in those days.

Harold Jackson, the greengrocer, came from Bewholme with his horse and rully once a week delivering fruit and vegetables. One wondered how he made a living as money was so scarce and most country people grew their own vegetables. In those days, as kids, we thought it was a great treat to get an orange in our stocking at Christmas as fruit was a luxury.

Richard Prescott was the butcher; he came round the village twice a week with pony and trap from his base in Brandesburton. Meat was very cheap, and in many cases was traded by the stone rather than the pound.

Charlie Patrick was the local carrier and lived at Skipsea. His form of transport was up market to most of the others. It was a large van with a wooden body built on it, which had a maximum speed of 20 miles per hour. He called at every house in the village to collect orders for their weekly requirements, and then went to the city of Hull to do the shopping for them.

The main item was groceries, but he would bring any article, even down to ironmongery. He delivered them on his way home, and would often be in the village as late as eight o'clock that night. He had different villages to shop for from Monday to Friday, and on Saturday he put seats in his van and took the local football teams to away matches; this completed a busy week.

Jos Wilson, poultry dealer, collected eggs weekly. He also bought old hens which were at the end of their laying life; these were known as boilers and would generally be eaten covered with a white sauce. He was an expert at checking whether the hens were laying eggs or not. Needless to say, if he happened to be short of boilers that particular week the cull would be a little more severe!

He also bought Christmas poultry; turkeys, ducks, geese and roasting chickens. Jos had a large trade in wild rabbits, one of the cheapest meats on the market. This was understandable as the countryside was overrun with rabbits: it was common place for a farmer to have a third of his cereal acreage wiped out by the pest.

Mr. Brown, a salesman for Stockills of Driffield, who were soft furnishings and furniture suppliers, would visit the village every other week for orders or any repairs.

Doctor Cree, the village doctor, journeyed from Beeford by motor cycle and sidecar to visit the sick in their homes, as most folk had no form of transport to get them to the surgery. He was a very tall, well-built Irishman, and was known by some people as a gentle giant. This, of course, was a joke; he didn't know the meaning of the word gentle!

He carried a pair of pliers and a sharp penknife to lance anything above skin level. He had never heard of injections or painkillers; you just had to grit your teeth and, hey presto, the job was done. He prescribed syrup-of-figs for 'movement' (his word), and after that you moved pretty quick, or else. For any stomach complaints he supplied you with a 'special' white emulsion mixture which he must have had patent rights on.

As a young lad I had bronchitis and became delirious: his recommended cure was castor oil. To get it down my throat they would nip my nose to stop me breathing, which gave me no alternative but to swallow. My last dose was 60 years ago and I can still taste the dam stuff. At eleven years old I broke my arm and the old doctor set it with two wooden splinters held together with bandages. Unfortunately he didn't get it quite straight, so it had to be broken again after three weeks and reset. I spent two days in hospital and six weeks with a plaster cast on. Thankfully he had much more sympathy when it came to paying the bills, and for the very poor there was no charge at all.

Mr. Morrow, the chemist from Hornsea, completed the list of tradesmen who serviced the village at that time. He only came once a month, with a selection of goods in his van.

We must not forget the men who came to the village once a week to deal with our sins. They did not come to sell us worldly goods, but to teach us the spiritual lessons of life.

The Church of England parson, who came from the parish of Beeford, held a weekly afternoon service, at three o'clock, in Dunnington Church, which was about half a mile up the road from our house. He would call at our house every week, just open the door and shout: "Are there any Christians today?" With mother a church warden and six children who hadn't much choice, he nearly always got his car full, leaving the surplus to walk the half-mile.

There was a Methodist Sunday School held in the Chapel every week, which took place in the morning and an evening service at six o'clock. This was generally conducted by a local preacher, as there was only one Minister for the Hornsea circuit. Most of the local preachers were farmers and some were more like comedians to us kids than religious preachers. There were times when we were reprimanded for laughing out of turn.

When leaving the Chapel we would hear the adults discussing the service and comments such as: "When he puts his Sunday clothes away, his religion goes with them." Yet we, as children, were expected to be whiter than white. As we became teenagers it was more difficult for mother to round us up for church and she discussed this problem with the parson. His reply was: "Don't let that worry you, they will be sure to go one day, even if it is feet first!"

So as you can see, unless wine, women or song entered your head, there was no need to leave the village, as everything was delivered to your doorstep.

Chapter Two

I STARTED Skipsea School in 1931 when I was three-and-a-half-years old. Apparently this was because I was a very mischievous young lad, and 'getting rid' of me for eight hours a day helped to take the pressure off at home. Discipline at the time was more important than the education. No wonder I always agree with people who say they like 'rum' lads.

To get to school, I rode on the carrier of my elder brother's bicycle until I reached the age of five, after which time I was considered old enough to pedal the three miles unaided. When cycling to school each morning the only person we would meet was the postman. Like us, he also travelled by push-bike. His delivery round was a nine-mile route, which covered a number of villages, as well as all the farms along the way.

Every morning we would greet him with: "Good morning Mr. Postman, could you please tell us the time?" He was a jolly man, and would reply "Good Morning," after which he would pause, take his watch out of his waistcoat pocket and tell us the time. This action was always followed by a witty remark. I remember now, it wasn't the time we were interested in, it was the jokes we liked, and he always made us laugh. This daily routine somehow seemed to make our journey shorter, and I'm sure the postman enjoyed meeting us too.

There was one section along the road which we never looked forward too, especially when the wind was in the east. It was known as 'Dixon's open fields'. This was the only stretch of road where there wasn't any shelter, there were no hedges at all. From here, the North Sea was two miles due east and, with the wind blowing off the sea, it was always very cold and bleak.

As we turned the corner into the open fields, direct in a straight line about a mile across the countryside, stood a beautiful big, red, square farmhouse, which I always admired. We never passed it as it was on the Hornsea road out of the village of Skipsea. It was ironic that 14 years later and beyond my wildest dreams, I bought that farm and lived in that farmhouse.

When the weather was very rough, torrential rain or a snow storm, father would transport us to school by pony and covered trap, so we were not in wet clothes all the day at school.

There were now four of our family going to school, and our dinners at midday were provided by our carrier's wife, Mrs. Patrick. The meals were organised on a contra-system; we took milk and farm produce each morning, and the balance was paid by cash. Her workload was kept to a minimum, as we were only allowed one plate for the two-course meal.

At the end of the first course, we were supplied with a slice of dry bread; you could say that was a second course, but it was actually to clean your plate for the pudding. As kids we called it 'fill belly'. The better job you made of removing the gravy from your plate, the better the pudding tasted! This meal arrangement continued for all the years our family were at school.

Skipsea school had two teachers — a husband and wife partnership, Mr. and Mrs. Turner. Mr. Turner was the head teacher, and taught the nine to fourteen-year-olds, while Mrs. Turner taught the infants and juniors. For any of the 'do-gooders' of today who are convinced that there is no such thing as a deterrent for misbehaviour, I am sure that an encounter with Mr. Turner would have changed their minds!

The school motto on a plaque on the wall was: 'If it is not right don't do it. If it is not true don't say it'. Anyone breaking the law knew the consequences without any more reminders. We were taught that punctuality was a part of life, and to be late for school was a punishable offence. There was no excuse for lateness due to bad weather conditions. No consideration was given either to the distance you had to travel to school; you were expected to be on time whether you lived three miles down the lane or just across the road.

The Skipsea school, along with Hunmanby Hall were, at that time, the only two Methodist Schools in the East Riding. I remember we did go on the occasional visit to 'The Hall', but the lads from Skipsea were not impressed as it was a private girls' school, and rather upper class for the likes of us.

In those days there were a lot of very poor families who struggled to feed and clothe their children. This was due to the fact that there was very little work to be had and no government support whatever. The order of the day was 'waste not want not'.

I know that those starving people would have been shocked beyond belief, had they experienced the recent burning of the 1,000 tons of good English beef. Hunger is a nasty thorn, and it had happened to many of them. We would try to help our school mates in some small way but, to put it in a nutshell, we were all pretty much in the same boat . . . damn poor. To be brought up in that era was probably the best education anyone could have had.

Home life was almost the same; you all worked together, and I mean worked. There was a strict regime for all the family. We all had jobs to do before we set off for school. We were allowed just half an hour morning and evening for the journey. We had to be home by four o'clock; there was no stopping to play with your pals and all shops were out of bounds.

Jobs in the evening included getting sticks and coals in for lighting fires, cleaning shoes for the morning, washing pots, feeding chickens, gathering and cleaning eggs and any seasonal jobs on the farm. As school lads the important jobs on the farm were haymaking and harvesting. During the school holidays we had to take the farm workers their lunches mid-morning, and in the afternoon we always included our own little food pack and joined in with the men.

We used to enjoy the threshing machine coming in. It was towed by a steam engine. We would watch the men setting it up to the stack, which was quite a performance. There seemed to be men shouting everywhere — 'Up a bit, back a bit'. Unlike our modern-day tractor which will move a fraction of an inch at a time, this monster used to jump backwards too much, and the machine would drop off the wooden blocks they were trying to set it on; next time it would jerk too far forward and come off the blocks again.

All this palaver was about getting the machine dead level. If it was not level the machine was not efficient. The corn would go over the 'back-end' on to the floor and not through the sieves into the sack. You only received payment for bagged corn.

Another thing we did as lads was unofficial really. On the day of the week that the stallion visited the farm, we would go into our hideout and watch them cover the mares. We didn't realise it at the time, but this was the only way they could increase horsepower on the farm! The owner of the stallion was generally a farmer and, in most cases, a well-to-do-one at that. He would employ a man to travel the stallion in the local area.

The man walked the stallion from farm to farm, calling once a week to try the mares, and cover any that were in season. He would walk 20 miles a day, six days a week, and would cover 50 to 70 mares in the Spring season. Every two or three years, the stallions would be moved to another area and a new one brought in to avoid breeding with their own progeny.

Sheep dipping was another highlight we looked forward too. This was done on contract. The contractor went from farm to farm by horse and buggy, with the dip tub and all other ancillaries loaded on it. He was a little man, five feet tall, but as broad as as he was long: he weighed in at 22 stones and swore like a trooper. He was known by everyone as Jip, which sounds more like a dog's name than a man's. He would come trundling into the yard, having travelled nine miles, sat on top of the tub.

The first job was to get Jip down to ground level, which took two men a lot of time and all their energy. The next job was to get the dip tub off the buggy. To achieve this they took the weight of the tub at one end, then pulled the buggy forward. It was at this point that Jip would shuffle underneath to get the tub right end up. The tub was made of wood and with it always being wet it weighed like lead.

Dipping always took place in the foldyard, so the day before Jip came preparations commenced. Two large holes were dug in the manure, the first exactly the right size to take the tub, the other just to one side to take the box that Jip stood in while he dipped the sheep. Jip was dressed in waterproofs, and wore a leather apron and a felt hat.

Once every dipping day the lads catching the sheep would accidentally drop a sheep into the tub, splashing poor old Jip in the face. Off would come the felt hat to dry his face then the air round that dip tub went 'blue'. The handlers wouldn't risk the trick again that day, but as they turned away from Jip to catch the next sheep they both had a smile on their faces. When dipping finished the last through the trough was the sheep dog. I don't think that dog liked dipping day one little bit.

The next job was packing up. The tub had to be emptied and dug out of the manure, and Jip's box also lifted out. It was a case of brute force loading them back onto the buggy. We always got the final laugh watching the two lads struggle to get Jip back on top of his tub. Once he was up there he couldn't get off until he reached home.

There were open fields a mile and a half up the road which were gated, so one of us young lads had to cycle in front of him to open the gates. As he went through the last gate he would throw down a thrupenny bit. It was quite a good tip; you didn't often get thrupence at one go in those days.

I remember three unusual machines, which were used on a regular basis on our farm in the early 1930s. There was a pump and engine system, a sail reaper and an Austin tractor. The former pumped water from a big dyke through 350 yards of pipeline into a 5,000-gallon tank. The tank, which was originally a ship's boiler, had been positioned high in the stock yard on concrete walls. Pipes with taps were connected to the tank, providing a supply of water to horse and cattle troughs by gravity. This was at a time when most farmers were still pumping water by hand, loading it onto a horse-drawn cart, and leading the water to their stock.

Secondly, there was the sail reaper, which was used to cut dry peas. At that time it was the only machine available which moved the crop sideways; this prevented the horse from trampling on the crop when cutting the next time round.

The design idea for the sail reaper, came from an old machine which had been made originally to cut the cereal crops. Man started inventing cutting machines as early as the 1790s to replace hand mowing with a sickle.

It was Patrick Bell's reaping machine, produced in a factory in Dundee in the 1830s, which was one of the first workable machines. It appears that the self-raking sail reaper and the reaper binder were being developed at the same time. English and American inventors of both machines were using different types of sails; the one on the reaper binder pushed the top of the crop towards the cutting knife, and on the sail reaper swept the crop from the knife, then off the platform onto the ground. This allowed the knife on the sail reaper to be driven much slower than on the reaper binder.

During the Victorian era the scythe replaced the sickle. It had a metal gathering rake with four tines attached to it, which left the

15

swath neat and tidy to make a sheaf. A part of the harvest force would follow the mowers to hand tie and stook the sheaves.

1860 saw the introduction of the clip reaper, which gave the farmers the option of mechanical mowing. Needless to say very few changed their system! This machine was what we now know as the grass reaper. It left the swath very untidy and not easy for the workers tying the sheaves. This system was then followed in 1870 by the sail reaper which increased the cutting rate but left the swath little better than the previous machine. So the work force had to be increased to follow this reaper to hand tie and stook the sheaves.

A year later only about a quarter of the British harvest was being done by mechanical means. A revolution came when F. J. Appleby invented the binder twine and a machine knotter. But the big step forward came in 1878 when McCormack introduced the string-tying reaper binder. This made harvesting much easier and reduced the labour force considerably.

Finally there was the twenty-five horsepower Austin tractor. It was actually powered by a motor car engine, and had flat iron wheels with a belt pulley on. Its sole use on the farm was to drive the rolling mill, which rolled oats for the cattle and horses. So the tractor stood in the stackyard, while the horses and staff went out to do the land work . . . One wonders if they had got it right!

Land in Holderness was farmed on a five-course rotation. About a third of the farm was permanent pasture, the remainder was arable. The rotation was wheat, barley undersown with white clover, wheat, followed by a break crop of either turnips, legumes or the field was fallowed, thus completing the rotation.

Land that was fallow was formed into ridge and furrow each year; this was to assist with its drainage. The idea was to form high points in the centre of the row of land drainage pots, and a low point immediately above each pot. This was created by setting a rig down the centre of the pots and ploughing both sides inwards, thus finishing with the furrow hole directly above the pot.

It was a very labour-consuming job as each row of pots in the field had to be found and marked before the ploughing could start. A skilled man would dig up a clump of earth and look to see if there was a mixture of soil and clay in the sod. If there was, this told him the soil had been dug out before and meant that he was not so far from the row of pots.

On the other hand if there were no such signs he would continue to take samples till he found them. Once he found the first row of pots he had a guideline. As land drainage was normally done at eleven yard spacing, once he found the first row of pots he had a guideline to continue his work, until every line of pots in the field was marked.

Staffing on the farm wasn't unlike the army. Each person had a rank and knew full well their pecking order. There was foreman who was 'head sir rag' — in other words the leading light over all staff, and always drove the best pair of horses. Next came waggoner and then third lad. There was a shepherd and a beastman. The latter was known as bullocky and was generally thrupence short of a bob.

On larger units where more staff were needed, each one of the former would have a lad up to the required numbers. The ratio of staff would be about two men per 100 acres and four horses. All farms were a bit like *'Old Macdonald'* — they had a little bit of everything. 'You didn't have all your eggs in one basket' then.

In the mid-Thirties our parents decided to purchase a car. Father smoked and mother had occasional help in the house. They made a pact; father gave up the smoking and mother agreed to manage without help. This saved them a grand total of £14, enough to purchase a second-hand Morris Cowley car. Father bought the car, which was from a good home and had been well maintained, in Hull.

Upon collection the salesman escorted him to the end of the tram lines on Holderness Road, and then he was on his own. That was the only driving lesson father ever had and he had never driven a car before in his life. There was very little traffic on the roads in those days, but one wonders what percentage of learner drivers today would have successfully completed the other 15 miles!

In 1937, a new Ford tractor and two furrow ploughs appeared on the farm. It had a water air cleaner and the clutch acted as a brake as well. Actually, until the oil warmed up it didn't respond to either, so consequently it needed at least ten yards to get stopped.

One morning I saw this tractor go straight through a five-barred gate, smashing it to bits. The driver didn't realise that there was what they called a retarding lever, which would have stopped the engine, and that was the only way of getting the thing stopped!

The plough was also anything but reliable. There was a rope from the plough to the tractor which, when pulled, jacked the plough out of the working position at each end of the field. This sometimes achieved the object, but on many occasions the plough would drop straight back in and continue to plough. So you could say you had little control of either the tractor or the plough.

The horse hoe was still being used in the 1930s. It was made to follow the eleven row corn drill, and had eleven four-inch pointed shares to go between the drill rows and remove the weeds, although it was impossible to remove weeds down the corn row. The implement was pulled by a single horse, one with a good temperament. This task also required a skilled man, as it was a very precise job and in many cases saved the crop from total extinction.

Chapter Three

O N 3rd September, 1939, the war broke out and there were unknown changes ahead for the Forties. The first big change in the Forties was the army call-up of most young men between the age of 18 to 35. This took the majority of workers off the land. The waggoners and third lads got a different rank and this ended the long established ranking of farm workers forever.

It also heralded the end of Martinmas. The 23rd November was Martinmas Day. It was held in all market towns throughout the country. All farmers requiring staff and any workers looking for jobs would be there. The farmer and worker would negotiate terms. Once they reached an agreement, the farmer gave his new employee a small amount of money known as a 'fest', and that was a binding contract for the next year.

The greatest fear in the early days of the war was that the Germans would attack us with gas bombs, so everyone was issued with a gas mask, and also an identity card, which had to be carried with you at all times. Not only were these frightful days, they were sad days. There were always reports of someone missing presumed killed, or being killed, whom you knew personally; very often an older lad from your own school.

It was amazing how everyone seemed to get used to the danger, and accepted the daily risks we were living in. Having said that, those who lost loved ones, were the people who really suffered. Life in those war-torn days was like a game of bridge, you never knew what the next hand dealt would bring, but whatever it did, you made the best of it and just carried on.

I left school in August, 1941, at the age of 14. There were academics in our family, but the brains had not been evenly distributed — so my secondary education was done on the farm. The day you left school you became a man, and were expected to do a man's job. During my first year working on the farm there were a number of jobs which I never looked forward to — threshing corn, fiddle drilling clover seed, leading first horse drilling turnips, and milking the house cows by hand!

By the time I started full-time work the threshing machine had changed from steam engine power to tractor power; this meant that the machine was quieter and much quicker to move and set up. The only person who seemed to enjoy threshing day was the owner of the machine. Not only did he get paid for the contract of the machine, he also carried the corn, so you could say he was on double pay.

It needed two people to carry the corn. They had to be very strong and fit to do this work, and most likely would have worked on a farm all their lives and seemed to have the knack of getting the bag in the right position on their back.

There were two men on the corn stack. One passed the sheaves and the other forked them onto the machine to the band cutter. He cut the band and passed the sheaf onto the feeder, collecting all the bands which had been cut at the knot. The person feeding the machine had to keep an even flow of the material all the time. This ensured all the grain would be threshed from the head, and if it went through in lumps, the machine was unable to do this. There were two on the straw stack, one forking the straw (who was known as the picker) to the other who was the stacker, and he or she stacked the straw. The other two who made the team of ten up, were generally juniors of the team and they carried chaff and pulls.

Chaff was the refined name: we always called it 'caff'. Caff was the separated husk of the corn, and was used for feeding livestock. Wheat caff was the best feed and always fed to the horses. Barley and oat caff was kept separate and fed to cattle. Pulls were short ends of straw, which dropped out of the end of the machine, and would not carry up the elevator with the straw.

All this material had to be carried away in sheets. As young lads we always called this job, 'the mucky end of the stick', as each night you were as black as the Ace of Spades, and there was no such thing as an easy day. Dust masks had not been invented, and quite a lot of what should have been in the sheet was down your throat.

The old hands used to tell us we should learn how to 'chow' (chew) twist; it was too strong to swallow, so they spit it out and all the dust with it. They all did this, so on threshing day it was as bad as ploughing with horses and being bombarded with seagulls all day.

When the machine was in the village, each farmer would send staff to help each other. This was known as tramp threshing, and you knew who would be away from home. Lunches were provided mid-morning and afternoon and apart from being at home, you only looked forward to the break, not the lunch. Caff on the farms except home farm, had to be carried up steps into stores above the horse stables, which made it hard work for lads who had just left school.

By this time there was a shortage of 100,000 workers on the land, and the greatest single resource filling this need was the Women's Land Army. There was a government request for volunteers between the age of 20 and 30 to join the Land Army, which attracted 1,000 young ladies.

Conscription started in 1941 and by 1943 there were 70,000 Land Girls working on British farms. Most of them admitted they thought it would be a good life, to get into the countryside and out of the towns where bombing was already taking place. What they didn't realise was the kind of life they had come to.

21

After four weeks' training they were paid the equivalent of £1.40p for a 50-hour week, and lodgings would cost them £1.25p so — like many more people, including all those in the armed forces — they were working long hours for nothing more than their keep.

You had to live through those times and see it personally to realise how everyone pulled together: money is of little importance when survival is the name of the game. There was little animosity among our own people: there was only one enemy, as we were all fighting the same cause — that was to destroy Hitler and his gang. As well as the Land Girls coming on to the land, we also had students and old age pensioners helping to solve the agricultural labour crisis.

All this took place as the politicians suddenly realised there was a shortage of food in this country, and many times in history wars had been won by starvation.

To give you some idea how desperate the situation was, these are the wartime rations for one person per week: 4 ozs. bacon, 8 ozs. sugar, 6 ozs. butter, 2 ozs. cooking fat, 1s. 2d. worth of meat, 3 ozs. cheese, 3 pints of milk. And per month: three eggs and a pound of preserves (jam).

Agriculture was needed again after nearly 20 years of depression. Are the politicians going to allow this to happen again? 'Dig for Victory' was the slogan issued to the nation; to bring every square yard into food production, but especially to the farming industry. Flower gardens disappeared almost immediately, and were turned into vegetable gardens; even chain linked fences, and any metal objects were confiscated to be melted down for arms. The farming industry virtually had to accept changes over night.

The War Agriculture Committee took charge of how the land should be farmed. This was a body of men, made up of Ministry advisers and some of the supposedly top farmers in each area. Naturally everyone did not agree with the choice, but to get the land of this country into maximum production, the powers-that-be had to start somewhere.

Any farmer, even on his own farm, who did not cultivate the land to a certain standard was turned off and his land confiscated and farmed by the W.A.C. At that time the agriculture in this country certainly needed a whack. Their first task was to get thousands of acres of virtually derelict land into production. Much of this was self-sown grass land, but had been arable before the depression. Most of the land, apart from the chalk lands on the Wolds, was deficient in lime, so they put a subsidy on lime to encourage farmers to correct the situation.

Many farms in Holderness, as well as on other heavy clay land throughout the country, were lying very wet, as the last generation of farmers had never paid any attention to dykes and drainage. A subsidy was introduced to cover half the cost to put new drains in where required and clean hundreds of miles of dykes and drains out.

As the old foreman used to say to my grandfather: "You can't grow corn in a piss-pot."

Horses were still the major power on the land and it was just as important to keep them in good order as it is a tractor in good repair today. Feeding horses to keep them fit was an art in itself: all food should have been consumed in half an hour. If any was left in the trough after that, they were either ill or getting too much food in the first place.

Wheat caff was put in a sieve to shake all the dust out, then rolled oats were measured and mixed with the caff. They had their meals at the same time as the workers, morning, noon and night. In winter, work started at half past five in the morning. You mucked them out, fed them and groomed them, and then went back to the farm house for breakfast.

After breakfast it was back to the stable to harness your pair of horses, and at half past seven prompt you were leaving the stackyard on your way to the field, always riding the nearside horse side-saddle. You knew full well you were going to get enough walking once you arrived at your plough. The same procedure happened again midday. You knocked off at twelve noon and started again at one o'clock. You would finish ploughing at half past five and each man would have ploughed one acre.

A verse of a poem I learnt at school always came to mind towards the end of the day when ploughing. It went:

'Up the field and down the field,
And once more round again,
With a keen wind blowing,
And a sky that looks like rain,
Gee up, gee up Dick Turpin,
And steady Rob my lad,
It's hard work is a man's work,
But a happy day we've had'.

Then it was back to the stable to feed your horses, then go for your tea. Then back after tea to groom them, bed them down with clean wheat straw, 'supper them up' which meant giving them a little hay and two mangoldwurzels (a type of turnip). Then back for bed at nine o'clock.

You didn't *'rock around the clock'* all night and *'rock, rock rock 'til the broad daylight'* in those days, because you were up and at it again quite a long time before the broad daylight. All this work among horses was done meticulously to ensure they were fit at all times.

There was also a lot of work among young horses, rearing them from foals to breaking them in to work at three-year-olds. Breaking young horses was very much like bringing up a family. 'If you hadn't got discipline by the time they were three years old, you were fighting a losing battle'. In other words, you had to be the master while they were still at the age of learning — which was the quickest period of their lives.

The first lesson was to put a halter on their heads and tie them to an object, which would not move, but in a safe place where they could not injure themselves. They always fought against this restriction, pulling backwards then suddenly lurching forwards: this was where the term 'swinging a horse' came from. Eventually you were able to lead the horse with ease, without the possibility of it taking you for a hundred yard sprint. That was lesson number one, and the most important one of all, for you had won the first battle and, I might add, without any cruelty.

The next lesson was for the youngster to gain confidence in you. When feeding, you would stroke it on any part of the body; this was known as handling the young horse. You would then lift each leg up in turn, to prepare it for the farrier when shoeing day came along. You trimmed and plaited the tail, so at a later date you would be confident you were not going to receive an unexpected kick up the backside.

This was all leading up to when the horse was two years old. The next job was to 'mouth it'. A bridle would be put on, with a metal bit placed in its mouth, and then backed into a single stall, and also a string tied on each side of the bit and to each side of the stall. Every time it moved forward the bit would tighten on the side of the mouth. The halter acted as a safety precaution as it limited how far the horse could go forward.

This training would be done three or four hours per day for two weeks, till the mouth was soft and the horse would respond to the reins. If you pulled the ring rein it would go to the right and, likewise, if you pulled the left it would go to the left.

The next exercise would be to drive it out in reins. The first time you would do this was in an enclosed area so, if things didn't go to expectation and the horse didn't respond to being driven and broke loose, you would not be chasing it round the district. This was a safety measure only, for a good horseman would be very confident this would not happen and very rarely did. It would then be taken into a field and circled; first driven one way round and then the opposite way. it was taught to go forward on demand, and reverse backwards by gently pulling both reins evenly together. While all this was going on you would be talking to it as a mother would be to her child.

The big day came for both man and beast when it was time to yoke the trainee. The traces — which were two chains, connected to each side of the horses collar — were hooked onto a swingeltree, which was a strong piece of wood used for pulling all implements connected with horses. It was then yoked to a very light load such as a railway sleeper, just so it felt the weight on its shoulders and got used to wearing a collar.

All this training was carefully monitored by the horse-breaker and he knew by experience when to take the next step forward. There was no exact timetable to each part of the job.

The grand finale was to yoke the young horse as a pair with a good old stalwart to start its working career. Each one was tied to the other: the young one was under control both by the driver and the older horse, and soon became a regular working horse.

Even with well trained horses you did get the occasional run-away. This was generally caused by a strange noise, or something they had never seen before. There was the odd serious accident in such cases, and also staff being kicked by horses. I suppose the safety officer today would require a kicking rail at the arse-end of the horse: whether he would want it nailing or bolting we'll never know!

Horses had to be taken to the blacksmith's shop to be shod and to keep their feet in good trim. The shop was three miles away, and to get two horses shod was half a day's work. If there was only one horse needed shoeing you would take a cart loaded with harrows to be laid, or any machinery repairs which needed doing. There were no electric welders, so all repairs were done with furnace and bellows.

Horse shoes were made from a straight piece of metal: it was heated until red hot, and then bent to the exact shape of the horse's foot. It was even placed on the hoof while still red hot, to make sure it was a perfect fit. The nail holes in the shoe were punched out while still hot, as there were no drills to do the job. When satisfied it was a perfect fit, it was cooled in a cold water trough, and then nailed onto the horse's hoof.

Laying the harrows, which were used for working the land, was also done with red hot metal. The worn-down teeth of the harrows were lengthened and shaped back to 'as new' condition, by heating both pieces of metal and braising them together; this was very skilled work.

Morley's blacksmith's shop had the first power hammer in this area. It was invented and made by them and was belt-driven by an engine which was adjusted to use waste oil or fuel. They were very skilled workers and consisted of a father and son partnership. It was an experience not to be missed for a young lad to visit this blacksmith's shop.

The relationship between the two was always on a knife edge, as often is the the case where there is a generation gap. It was difficult for them to see eye to eye, but in that shop you had always to keep your eyes open in case of flying objects. Many a time there would be an argument.

All of a sudden a hammer would be thrown to the floor and it was miraculous how it fell on the other one's foot — then all hell was let loose. As a young teenager who was not allowed to answer his father back, this was unbelievable and almost as entertaining as going to the cinema and seeing a Wild West show.

Horses were very much like human beings. They were individual characters; there were no two horses alike. There were hard workers and those that had to be driven, and there were quiet ones and flighty ones.

We had a mare called Blossom, and she was a very bad-tempered

27

one and would not have been on the farm if I had been in charge. She never kicked out at human beings, but very often had kicking sessions when yoked to implements fitted with a pole, such as wagons, reaper binders and grass reapers; the pole separated the two horses, but acted as a steering agent.

There were times when she actually broke the pole. The only way to stop her doing this was to put Stockholme tar on a piece of band put it in her mouth, over her ears and tie them down. We never knew which part of this exercise was responsible for stopping her kicking, but it did.

I often wondered why the Governor put up with this but she was his favourite horse, and the best worker on the farm and he liked both men and beasts with a bit of fire in their bellies. She only had one foal in her life, a grey colt named Royal. He was just the opposite to his mother, which proves the point — like doesn't always breed like.

One morning I was given the job of taking the harrows to the blacksmith's shop to be laid. It was a bitter cold morning with snow blowing all ways, and much too cold to ride on the cart. I walked leading Royal with the halter. Under normal circumstances he was a very quiet horse. We came to a patch of road with no snow on it, and the wheels suddenly made a clatter which startled him. He set off at a gallop. He didn't leave me standing, he left me flat on my back on the road, with the cart wheel missing me by an inch. This was my lucky day; it could have been a serious accident.

It was more than your life was worth to have to go home and report a runaway horse, so I decided to go to a neighbouring farmer for help. The joddle pin on the cart had broken which allowed the cart to tip up and stop the runaway. The farmer was very kind and sent his foreman with a new pin to mend the cart, and help me to yoke up and get on my way again.

A job with horses I never looked forward to was leading first horse drilling turnips. Foreman led shaft horse with a leading stick.

He walked in a straight line down the previous row, keeping the stick in a rigid position — this assured he kept the rows straight and even, for working down with the scruffle at a later date. We would just get settled down to what I thought was a reasonable speed, and there would be a great bellow: "Go on, gee up." Both horses leapt forward, shot up two gears, and were off like hell again.

The next job I disliked was fiddle drilling. It was mainly undersowing Spring barley with clover seed. Foreman led the way and I followed on. You were taught to march army fashion, left right, left right. On the left your hand was pushing the fiddle stick; on the right you were drawing it back, and this was the rhythm for the day. We took a break of five yards wide across the field. He didn't take steps of a yard — they were twice that size; mine being smaller meant I was walking much faster and also fiddling faster to cover the same ground. He had been doing this for donkey's years; his old feet were as tough as leather.

By midday I had blisters on both feet and a sore hip, where the drill box had been chaffing. After dinner we struck off again. The old foreman was marching leisurely along, with a smile on his face. I was hobbling behind him with tears in my eyes. Nobody cared: they had all gone through it, now it was my turn.

Other jobs we had to learn in the early Forties included stacking sheaves of corn, and the most important point was topping the stack up to keep it dry. I was very fortunate to have one of the best stackers in the area to teach me. He was Mr. Fred Robinson, a retired farmer in his mid-seventies, who had come back to help with the harvest due to the war.

He and his brother had farmed Dunnington House Farm, and people came from miles away to see their stacks. They were all stacked in pikes. A pike was a round stack with a pointed top as the word suggests. All the stacks were shaved and when they were finished there was not a straw out of place.

The stacks were thatched to keep them dry, which was a very

labour-consuming job, but the pride they took in their stacking made it one of the best, and as tidy a stackyard as there was in the East Riding of Yorkshire. We always stacked corn in oblong stacks, six yards wide and twelve yards long. This was the right size for a day's threshing, and would take about ten acres of cereals to complete a stack.

Another skilled job was hedging which was done on a rotational basis. All hedge bottoms were mown out with a scythe, then the hedges were trimmed with a slasher and all the debris cleaned up and burnt. Every year there was a proportion of hedge cut down to ground level. There were two reasons for this, the main one being to get new growth right from the bottom of the hedge. This was a similar principle to pruning roses.

If there was a gap in the hedge, you left a straight piece of thorn, the length of the gap, then cut it half way through, and bent it over to fill the gap, putting a stake in to tie it down and keep it in place. The idea was in a few years' time when the hedge grew up, there would be no more gaps and it would make an excellent fence, and would not need any more fencing.

The other reason was to use the long thorns to fence permanent pastures. They were loaded onto wagons and taken where required. Each one was individually placed on the boundary of the field with a pitchfork, to form what was called a dead fence. The cut end of the thorn was pushed into the bush end one by one, and this formed a very tidy stock-proof fence.

All these jobs were labour intensive but labour was dirt cheap, and no materials had to be purchased. They did not write cheques out in those days, unless there was no alternative. We hand-hoed all cereals (thistles and docks being the main weeds) and we also gapped sugar beet and turnips by hand. All foldyard manure was loaded and spread by hand. This didn't take much learning, it was more 'brute force and ignorance'.

Chapter Four

THE Governor always bought a consignment of Irish cattle to graze his pastures in the Spring. When these cattle arrived they were in very poor condition as they had been out wintered, but once put onto lush pastures they grew like mushrooms and soon became big and strong beasts.

Initially, a dealer would go to Ireland and purchase cattle on behalf of a number of farmers, who each required their own type of beast. They were transported by ship to either Holyhead or Liverpool and then by rail to their final destination. In our case this was normally to Hornsea station which was six miles from our farm.

One of us lads would be taken to Hornsea to drove these cattle home. The Governor never sent two men to do a one man job and, in his view, this only needed one! Going through the centre of Hornsea town with upwards of thirty cattle would have tested any drover.

You nearly had a heart attack when a beast stopped to look at its reflection in the window of the jeweller's shop. Stepping forward warily to move it on, unsure of which way it might lurch, you could only hope that it didn't choose to go straight forward through the jeweller's window. Luckily this never happened to me, but it had been known in a few cases.

The least opening into a garden or a yard always seemed to attract one beast through it and along the route there were many such openings! While you were busy getting one animal back on to the road, another would be exploring someone else's garden, therefore you were on tenter hooks all day.

Not only did you walk the six miles down the road, you also walked half as much again viewing other people's property not always as a welcome guest! As it was wartime there was always that togetherness, and the townsfolk coped with such incidents and the country way of life, much better than they do today.

Remember, these cattle were coming on to British farms to be fattened to keep that one shilling and tuppence worth of rationed meat on everyone's table. If only we'd had those vegetarians around then, we meat eaters would have had double rations, but regrettably they didn't exist.

On one occasion the train was unable to get to Hornsea and the cattle only landed as far as Beverley station. This meant a twelve mile drove just twice the normal distance from our farm. You've guessed it or I wouldn't have mentioned it . . . who the drover was that day? A twelve-mile hike with a little more thrown in trying to keep them on the track wasn't the most exciting day's work to look forward to, but as the Governor always said when he saw you weren't too pleased with your orders for that day: "While you're doing that, you do nothing else."

Fortunately these cattle were tired when released from the railway wagons after their long sea and rail journey. Luckily they didn't behave like our own stock who, when turned out to grass, would gallop from one end of the field to the other for at least half an hour.

When they had been driven clear of the town and out into the country, they would settle down to graze the grass along the roadside as they were hungry and then wander on in their own sweet way. This made the droving much more leisurely. In fact, the job could have been a very pleasant day out if the manpower had been doubled, but this was not the Governor's style.

What a difference it would have made with one person up front closing the gates and steering the cattle past open driveways. Also, the extra man could have warned on-coming traffic — what bit there was — that a herd of cattle was approaching.

This proved to be correct as, on the Beverley journey, tragedy struck. Thick fog came swiftly down at the village of Routh, a truck came round a blind corner, straight into the herd, seriously injuring one of them. Mr. Smith, who had the farm on this bad corner, came to my rescue and suggested that I put the cattle into his field for the night and see what the weather was like in the morning. He helped to organise transport to get the injured animal to the slaughter house and me back home.

This was an unusual incident as there was very little traffic on the roads and the most likely vehicles you would meet was an army convoy travelling very slowly. At that time livestock transport was available as the casualty was moved to the slaughter house by one, but this cost money. There was no need to pay for wheels, when each beast had four legs and a lad had two. The following morning I returned to Routh and got the cattle back on to the road and completed the journey.

Eventually the Irish cattle traders started to bring their own animals over the water and trade them. There were cattle pens available in most market towns, generally not far from the railway station; so then the Governor usually went to York and bought his own requirements direct from the dealer. This ended the job of droving as the distance was 40 miles and therefore father had to succumb to livestock transport. At York, the holding pens for the cattle were situated without the city walls near Walmgate Bar.

Cattle were on show one day a week and, as would be expected, the Irish were slick salesmen. There were normally twelve to fifteen of them showing cattle, each with two or three pens. As you walked up to a pen the dealer whose cattle they were would be there like a flash.

In his Irish accent he would say: "Are you looking for a load of good beasts today ser? I've got some great cattle here, they'd just do your job; do ye want to sey'em out?"

If you were interested you'd say that you'd like a look at them, being careful not to over commit yourself or he would put a price on them in no time. These salesmen didn't miss a move and it wasn't easy to keep ahead of them. So the cattle would be released straight on to the road, which was the main route through York. It is hard to imagine now how cattle could have been paraded along that particular stretch of road.

If the cattle didn't suit your purpose you would tell the man that you were going to have a look a bit further down the line and then come back to him. It was always hell's own job to get away from them. You were just not allowed to walk peacefully down the line and select the cattle that you liked the best. It was the same procedure as you came to each salesman; they were going to sell you their beasts by hook or by crook.

When you'd finally done the round and found the type of beast to suit your need and then had a look at them parading the highway, it came to bargaining time. It was necessary for you to be just as crafty as they were, as the asking price was always much greater than what they would eventually be prepared to take. Once you got the price within striking distance, you would then threaten to go a little further down the line to do your business. You had to squeeze them as you do a lemon to get the last little drop!

During the final bartering, the salesman would be holding the palm of his right hand out and, when you'd reached the price you were prepared to pay, you slapped his hand with the flat of your own right hand and the deal was done and dusted.

Chapter Five

ON MARCH 11th, 1942, my grandfather, on my mother's side of the family, was retiring from farming. He held a sale, which was described as:

'The whole of his Live and Dead Farming Stock viz.'

10 Horses:

Chestnut Mare, Violet, 9 years old. Dark Brown Mare, Smart, 10 years old. Chestnut Mare, Tidy, 7 years old. Black Mare, Diamond, 7 years old. Black Gelding, rising 7 years old. Bay Mare, rising 6 years old. Black Colt, Jack, 3 years old. Black Colt, Bob, 3 years old. Brown Colt, Tom, 3 years old. Brown Filly, Metal, 2 years old.

49 Beasts:

6 Bullocks, 2 years old. 2 Heifers, 2 years old. 9 Heifers, 18 months old. 5 Steers, 15 months old. 3 Heifers, 15 months old. 10 Heifers been running with Bull since October 4th including 4 Black and White. 10 Cows been running with Bull since December 17th. 1 Drape and 1 Roan Shorthorn Bull.

200 Sheep:

70 Masham Ewes in Lumb to Oxford and Suffolk Ram. 45 Banffshire Ewes in Lamb to Oxford and Suffolk Ram. 80 Cross-Bred Lambs. 3 Rams.

25 Pigs:

9 Saddleback Gilts in Pig. 16 Large white Gilts in Pig.

Machinery:

Fordson Tractor on Irons. Ransome 3-Furrow Plough. Bentall

*Rolling and Grinding Mill. Choppy Cutter for Power. Portable
Copper.*

Implements:
*3 wagons. 2½-Ton Spring Rully. 3 Heavy Carts. 6 ft. Deering
Binder. 6 ft. McCormich Binder. Albion Grass Reaper. Hornby
Corn Drill. Ransome Cultivator. 3-sheaf Press Drill. Bobbin Drill.
Hay Spinner. Horse Rake. Parmitter Harrows. 2 Sets Chisel
Harrows. 2 sets Wood Harrows. 2 Sets seed Harrows. 3 Scrufflers.
2 Cambridge Rollers. Corn Shim. 3 Ransome Diggers. Iron Ran-
some Plough. Spring Cart. Weigh and Weights. Turnip Chopper.
Cake Mill. Winding Barrow. Fiddle Drill. 8 Wire Nets. 10 Sheep
Troughs. Net Stakes. Lamb Feeder. Paraffin Tank (250 galls.). 5
Tumbrils. Wagon Sheet. Shelley Board. 24 Sheep Bars. Draughts. 6
Pig Troughs, etc. Usual small tools for 350 acres.*

2 Hen Houses. 10 Couples of Hens. Milk Cooler and Stand.

*Harness. 10 Horse Collars. Cart Saddle. 10 Pairs Blinders. 10
Pairs Backbands. Set of Breaking-In Tackle. String, etc.*

The farm was known as Sproatley Grange and was not unlike *Old
McDonald's Farm;* a little bit of everything, but this was a typical
sale at the time for a 350-acre farm.

It was notable that horses at the sale made up to £70 each, which
was the same figure my father had paid for them way back in 1921.
So it had taken 21 years for the price of horses to get back to the
same value again after the long farming depression.

In 1940, as a thirteen-year-old, I spent three weeks of my school
holiday helping my grandfather to harvest at Sproatley Grange. At
the end of the three weeks he paid me £1 and that was the first time
in my life I had ever received such a sum.

It was ironic that my grandfather on my father's side of the
family had also farmed this farm in previous years.

His wife died of typhoid at the age of 39, which she contracted
from the pump water supply . . . I often wondered what the family
attraction was to this farm! To me it was not a very desirable farm

and one I would not have been keen to farm; but circumstances alter such cases in this life so you don't always get where you want to be.

In April, 1942, the Governor rented an adjoining 320-acre farm, which doubled his acreage. The rent was 17 shillings an acre. Low Bonwick was a run-down farm with many problems, hence the small rent. It was infested with rats and rabbits, and a third of the farm was bad old pasture, and what little grazing there was, the rabbits about ate it. These old pastures were in ridge and furrow, the centre being two feet higher than the furrow. One wonders how this was done as these fields had never been ploughed for at least a hundred years, so one would assume this was done by hand.

If Low Bonwick had not quickly been improved, it would have been a prime target for take-over by W.A.C. and farmed by them on your behalf. So eight acres of land, covered with gorse bushes, had to be cleared. They were pulled up by a horse and then burnt. This was the first step in a rabbit-clearance exercise. We used gas and any other means to rid the farm of rats and rabbits.

Ploughing these old pastures out became compulsory, which was not an easy task. The equipment we had on the farm at the time was unable to do the job. By this time W.A.C. had set up a contracting business, and had acquired heavy tackle suitable for the work. They came with high-power crawler tractors, heavy disc harrows, ploughs and bulldozers. All these machines had been imported and had never before been seen by the farming community.

The first job was to level the land, as big tackle could not work on uneven land, so this heralded the end of landing up. There was a five-inch mat of turf and roots before you came to the soil. This was disced several times, chopping the turf into small blocks. It was left fallow until all the grass was dead and then ploughed in with a very large two furrow plough. The furrow width was eighteen inch and the trash was ploughed in 14 inches below ground. Needless to say the grass was never seen again. This was maiden soil with humus contents the likes of which we as farmers had never experienced before. You could say that this was the goose that laid the golden egg!

Suddenly, a third of the farm became prime land for cereal growing. This allowed some of the old arable land to be sown to grass leys. The order of the day was two blades of grass should be grown, where one had done before. I think in layman's terms that meant doubling the output. This actually increased output many times more, over both the new grass leys and cereals on the old pastures.

A new type of farming had been created, called ley farming. The new leys were left in grass for two to three years to build up fertility, then the land would be ploughed out. This was done on a rotation system across the whole arable area. The old pastures were being sown with cereals, mainly wheat, on a regular basis. Farm output was increased beyond belief and fertility in those old pastures was as good as money in the bank. Even 50 years later it is still possible to identify these old pastures.

By this time it became compulsory to grow potatoes and sugar beet on a percentage of your acreage. These were two crops which had never been grown on the farm. In fact, very few potatoes had ever been grown on the heavy land in Holderness. Potatoes became a major part of the diet and as cane sugar had ceased to arrive from abroad, beet sugar was produced at home. Not only was food scarce, you were unable to get tractors or farm machinery without a permit; in other words they were on ration!

Having increased the size of the farm to double its acreage, the Governor was able to apply for a larger tractor, which had to be imported from overseas. Importation of machinery was a high risk business as the enemy tried to sink every ship as a means of keeping output down. This meant that if you qualified for a tractor your name was put into a hat and when the next consignment arrived it was a matter of luck as to whether your name would be drawn.

Father came up trumps and the tractor he drew was an Allis Chalmers Model U on spade lug wheels (iron wheels). It had a 35-horsepower engine and cost £410. It looked massive on side the Fords and Fergusons we were used to seeing.

In 1932 Allis Chalmers tested a set of aircraft tyres on their model U. These proved to be a break-through in tractor development, and it became the first tractor to work efficiently on the land and then travel on the road. Rubber tyres did not seem popular in Britain: many farmers were concerned about punctures and therefore preferred iron spade lug wheels.

So with the new Allis Chalmers we were able to use a three-furrow plough and the Fordson tractor we had could pull a two-furrow plough — thus giving us a ploughing force of five furrows, which meant that horse ploughing then came to an end forever.

A few horses were still kept on to be used in a smaller scale for the odd jobs, such as horse-raking stubble, leading straw into the cattle yards, scruffling roots, spreading lime slag and fertilisers, as well as leading water from the pond on the new farm for the cattle.

At this point of time, our bullocky (stockman) gave a week's notice; the week ended Saturday at midday. Three out of four of us lads were working on the farms. My eldest brother went to live on the new farm and the two of us left at home became joint bullocky overnight. I found myself with two house cows to milk on Saturday night, dancing night.

I was a young teenager and had never ever milked a cow in my life. I had been sat there pulling tits for half an hour, my hands were aching like hell and I'd got about two pints in the bottom of the bucket. I made up my mind there and then. If I was going to have anything to do with tits in my life, they were not going to be those sort!

By this time the village was seeing quite a lot of H.M. Forces. The Manor House had been confiscated. There was only Miss Dixon and her housekeeper living there and they had to move into the flat at the end of the house, which had previously been the maid's quarters. The front of the house, which had prime position, became the officers' mess. The remainder was converted into Red Cross and medical quarters.

Miss Dixon was now a middle-aged Victorian-like lady and had lived at the Manor all her life. Since the loss of the Squire she had inherited the estate and was now Father's landlady. During her life she would have had very little contact with men apart from her father, so to suddenly be surrounded by young officers who lived for today and to hell with tomorrow, was a new experience for our Miss Dixon.

The officers held a party one night and the drink was flowing freely. There was a fair drop of beer on the room floors and officers were dancing on the lawn in their underpants. It was too much for the Victorian lady, so she went to sort them out — not very success-fully I might add, as you can imagine in those conditions.

When the officers told the tale they said that it was the best night's entertainment they had ever had and would not forget it for the rest of their lives.

Army manoeuvres and training was a regular occurrence on the farm. This could happen day or night: they were able to confiscate any building or part of the farm without prior notice or permission. Things could be quiet, with not a soul in sight when you left the farm in the evening. Next morning it would be like a small town. The army had moved in during the night and the buildings had been taken over. Dozens of soldiers had bedded down in the granary and any other building where it was warm enough to get a night's sleep.

I remember going to let the hens out one particular morning, only to find a soldier asleep in his bag. He had spent the night with the chickens! He had arrived on the farm at two o'clock in the morning freezing cold and the only warm place he could find was the hen house. He had been a city schoolteacher and had no idea that chickens had fleas on them, but he said that they hadn't bothered him. I suppose if you were dumped on a strange farm in the middle of the night and as flaked out as those lads were, things like fleas would be of little importance and fancy sleeping quarters were the last thing on their mind.

Events like this disrupted the whole farm. It brought all farming activities to a standstill. One never knew whether they were there for a few days or if it might be a week and no one could give you any information. You just had to wait till they disappeared as all their movements were secretive. The lads themselves didn't know their next move; in many cases it would be to a port for overseas service.

There were times when army officers in charge of these manoeuvres would try to get accommodation in our home. They were not able to confiscate, as we were a big family and had no empty rooms. Our parents would never refuse, so furniture in the dining room would be pushed to one end and the chairs moved to another room, in order to make space for eight sleeping bags down the centre. This again was an example of how the whole community worked together in difficult circumstances; to fight a war, which had to be won.

There was another occasion when army trucks were on the move through the village, It was a slow journey for a long convoy down a single track road and when there was an oncoming vehicle everything came to an immediate halt.

I remember some of the lads in the trucks, which stopped near the farmhouse, asked for a drink of water. All drinking water came from an outside pump and was stored in a bucket in the house. The lads brought their mugs and filled them from the bucket. This was empty in seconds and before we could get the water bucket refilled the lads spotted two buckets outside the house which were full of separated milk for the pigs. These also were drunk in seconds, as the minute the convoy started to move on they all had to be ready to go or they would have been in serious trouble.

Not only were the troops thirsty they were hungry as well, as they were surviving on what was known as iron rations. These were just basic amounts of food to keep them going and were part of the training all soldiers went through before they went abroad to fight. I suppose the lads at the time would think that it was tough going, but when they got to the front line I expect that they looked back on it as a picnic.

Wartime altered everyone's life in different ways, according to your age. Our parents were facing the second war of their lives within 20 years. Just as technology was starting to change in farming, it had changed in warfare. It had gone from horsepower in the First World War to 'airpower' in the Second.

Each evening we would count our bomber aircraft, as they left for Germany loaded with bombs to drop on military targets and German cities, knowing full well that some of them wouldn't be making the return journey.

Chapter Six

AS A teenager I was a member of the Driffield Young Farmers' Club and went to the meetings once a week. The only other evening functions at that time were the weekly dance classes at Bewholme village hall, with Gus on the piano and Jim on the drums, and the odd social event on a Saturday night.

I will always remember one particular social evening: we were being entertained by a magician. He was showing us a flea jumping out of a match box, when a bomb dropped within 40 yards of the village hall. All the lights were quickly put out and everyone laid flat on the floor until the all-clear sounded. Everyone was taught this drill. If you heard a bomb or gunfire in the vicinity, you dropped face downwards wherever you were and in whatever you were wearing. This reduced the target by about ten times, so the chance of survival was much greater.

Between the villages of Dunnington and Bewholme there was an anti-aircraft and searchlight site. This was manned by 12 soldiers and on our journey to these functions we were always challenged by a soldier with a loaded gun.

The instructions were: "Halt who goes there; friend or foe?" The answer was always "friend" and the reply came back: "Advance to be recognised." You then were asked to produce your identity card and then allowed to pass by. This procedure was carried out every time you passed this point. Even though these lads got to know us quite well, they had no option but to carry out this drill.

One evening two of these soldiers were walking the four miles back to camp from Beeford where they had been to the nearest pub for a drink, when bombs started to drop around the village. On these occasions it always seemed like a lull after the storm; everything went dead quiet and we would all go outside to see what the damages were, if any.

In the distance that night we heard what we thought was a horse running down the road. Father got his car out and went to investigate. It turned out to be one of the soldiers running as fast as he could to get help for his mate, who had been hit by shrapnel and had a serious wound to his leg. He was put in the car and taken to the doctor's to receive attention to his wound, before being taken to hospital. That ended the soldier's days in the army. He had received his injury before he had time to drop face downwards or this wouldn't have happened.

I remember well an occasion in the early Forties. The threshing machine pulled into the stackyard late one Saturday afternoon, to set it up ready for Monday morning. Our village was very small and young ladies were very sparse to say the least! It got to be 7.30 on the Monday morning, the worst day of the week, the worst time of the day and the worst job on the farm. How much nearer hell can you get than that . . . when four beautiful young ladies appeared in our stackyard? I thought the good Lord had sent four angels and when the foreman threw them caff sheets, I knew he had, for I had got promotion at last.

I was put on to the straw as picker; this job involved using a pick fork to push the straw to the stacker. These poor Land Girls had never been on a farm before and didn't even know that there was such a thing as a threshing machine. The previous week they had been working in the city as chemist assistants and hairdressers. They had changed their combs overnight for caff rakes.

By dinner time that first day, to say those young ladies had deteriorated was an understatement! They were all weeping, they had sore hands and blistered feet. I never knew how much more damage they had that was not showing, but it looked considerable.

There was only one place for them to go and that was the farmhouse, for mother to tend their wounds. Having brought six kids up, she almost had the qualifications of a nurse. At this point I must record that while all this had been going on, I had quickly received demotion back to the caffhole. Those four young ladies had been carrying caff and pulls which was a two-man job, so staff had to be moved around to complete the day's threshing.

Needless to say they didn't carry any more that day, but three months later those same young ladies were filling the places of four men and that was their job for nine months of the year. The other three months they were contracted out on to farms to help with summer jobs such as harvesting.

The only job they were unable to do was carry corn. Most corn was carried up steps into the granary. Peas and beans were weighed in 19 stones, wheat in 18 stones, barley in 16 stones and oats in 12 stones. There were four bushels in one bag, there were two bags in a quarter and five quarters of barley weighed one ton. You always referred to quarters threshed a day and corn would be drilled at three bushels an acre.

Unlike today, drilling took much more time and was spread over a longer period. Wheat was the main crop sown in the autumn. It was never sown before the eleventh of October otherwise the plant would have been too forward; this was known as being proud. There was a saying which went: 'Proud wheat and proud women would break any farmer!' Sowing in some seasons would go on until Christmas. With a ten-horse team, three to four acres drilled a day was a good output; that was, weather permitting.

Later sowing was the only method available for controlling diseases. Mildew was the most likely one to affect such crops and the later sowing allowed more time for cleaning the land. There were no sprays to kill the weeds or control diseases and nothing to shorten or stiffen the straw. With straw lengths between four and five foot, it was a real problem keeping even a reasonable crop standing over end and a laid crop reduced production by half.

Spring sowing would start with barley in mid March followed by oats. Peas, if grown, would not be sown before the 12th April and then root crops after that. There was always some late sowing on the turnip field where hogs would be folded. This would stretch into May.

As the sheep finished eating a fold, the nets would be removed and the land ploughed and sown. When farmers met they used to ask each other if they were sown up; more than likely the answer would be: "Why, we're ploughed up to sheep." This meant that they had not finished sowing, but were as near to it as they could be until the sheep had eaten all the turnips. In short, the drilling started on 11th October and didn't finish until May the following year.

Today any farmer using such a system would have no chance of survival and arable production would be reduced by at least two thirds. What a different picture today, with a surplus of every type of food you care to mention.

In those days the professors and scientists were inventing warfaring equipment and the only poison which was of any concern to them was the German's gas bomb. There were no questions asked about British food as there was no guarantee that everyone's belly would be full, and it is only people with full bellies who ever complain about food.

Harvest was a time of year that everyone looked forward to, even though it was all hard work and long hours. It just seemed to be the final job of the year which brought all the year's labour to fruition.

The first crop to be harvested was dried peas for human consumption. These were cut with the sail reaper then left a few days, according to the weather. They were then turned twice to dry on the other side. In a dry season they would only be turned twice after every rain, to keep the bottom peas from moulding.

Every time the peas were moved there was a certain amount of loss, and in very wet seasons there were times when there was a total loss. Peas were known as a gentleman's crop, because you only expected a good harvest every other year. When it was a good harvest the peas were bright in colour with no stains on them, which made them a very valuable crop, and a premium would always be paid. The peas were left in the stack for at least two months before threshing. This finished the drying procedure.

Cereals would follow straight on; they were wheat, barley and oats. All were cut with the reaper binder, with winter wheat generally being cut first. Three horses were used when reaping and they were on shift work. This meant that they were changed every four hours, as the work was very hard.

One man, who was the driver, would ride astride of the nearside horse. He had a flat waterproof saddle to sit on: this wasn't in case he wet his pants but to keep him dry from the sweat off the horse.

Another man rode the binder and carried a long pole. This was used to keep the off end point of the binder clear when going through laid patches. He also operated the sails of the binder, up or down according to the height of the corn.

Once the binder started dropping the tied sheaves out, the workforce moved in and started to stook the crop. You picked two sheaves up, one under each arm, walked into the centre of six rows and stood them up in a triangular fashion. This was achieved by putting the heads together at the top and the arse of the sheaves at the bottom, on the floor.

Twelve sheaves placed together made a stook. Stooking took place to allow the corn to dry, as if they had been put straight into the stack, they would have gone mouldy and wasted the whole lot.

All cereals were harvested in very much the same fashion, but the barley would have been undersown with clover. This was sown with a fiddle drill, after the barley crop was well established late in the Spring. So when the barley was harvested there were small clover plants growing in the stubble. These small plants could only stand to be covered by a stook for a week, all the stooks had to be moved to another part of the field, to ensure the clover seed survived. This job would be done in the morning or on a damp day when no other harvesting could be done. Moving wet sheaves which had already been stooked once was not a very exciting prospect, but as the Governor had said before; "While you are doing that you're doing nothing else."

Leading the corn to the stackyard was a very important part of the harvest. The corn had to be in good fettle, meaning it had to be dry and ready to stack. Wheat could be stacked before the barley, because it lay more open than the barley sheaves and air could circulate easier. In fact, wheat would often be stacked on dampish days and in the mornings; then in the afternoon when the sun was shining you would lead and stack the barley. These decisions had to be made on a daily basis, but it was most important to get the barley right to avoid having a stack of corn wasted.

The manpower needed for leading the corn was two men on the stack, one stacking, the other picking (meaning, passing the sheaves to the stacker). Three men each with a wagon drawn by two horses. They loaded their own wagon and roped it down to make sure they got to the yard with a full load, where they teamed it with a pick fork (pitch) on to the stack.

The other man required was in the field forking the sheaves on to the wagons. This was usually done by the Governor: he always put two sheaves on to the wagon at a time and they were always facing the right way for the loader, thus making his job easier. This was good thinking. The Governor knew if he was forking two sheaves at a time, five other workers were not hanging about.

Someone once said to me — from what they had heard about my father — he must have been a slave driver. My reply was: "No way was he a slave driver. A slave driver is behind with a whip. He always led the pack up front and when you had been in his company all day, sleeping at night was no problem."

Any extra staff needed at harvest time would be Irishmen. They came across in droves for the harvest months, and would be paid a fixed salary for the month. All their food had to be provided from the farmhouse, but sleeping quarters were in the granary, so you can see that the granary was serving many purposes! It was quite fortunate beer did not have to be supplied in the deal, for if it had the economics of the exercise would not have been viable.

On one occasion the end of their month came and very little harvesting had been done; this was due to the wet weather. There was no way of persuading them to stay for a further period. Their next move was to Lincolnshire to pick potatoes. This was done by 'tack' (a fixed price per acre) and enabled them to earn double the money they could harvesting in Yorkshire. In other words, they were filling in time with us until the potatoes were ready to pick.

Chapter Seven

T HE unconditional surrender came to battered Europe on the 7th May, 1945, at 2.41 a.m. The 8th May, 1945, became known as V.E. Day. Suddenly it was all over and Britain took to the streets to celebrate victory. Five years of wartime was forgotten, temporarily at least, in a blaze of coloured flags, fireworks and floodlights.

London set the pace and every city and town in the country followed suit. Fifty thousand people gathered in London to hear the Prime Minister broadcast over loud speakers. He said that although Japan remained to be subdued, the war in Europe would end at midnight. "Advance Britannia," he proclaimed. "Long live the cause of freedom, God save the King."

The churches were full of thankful people. The country went wild; there was dancing in the streets, people were kissing strangers and this went on throughout the night.

I was 17 years old at the time and in my diary on the 9th August (my birthday) I had written: 'Sweet 17 and never been kissed'. These celebrations ended that! I had only just been allowed the freedom to roam; this coincided with the end of the war. Until then my movements had been restricted to the local village hall events, under supervision, of course. Now I was hitting the limelight and going to town. Our main venue was the Floral Hall at Hornsea and the odd Young Farmers' Club dance at Bridlington or Driffield.

One Saturday night at the Floral Hall a pal and myself danced all the evening with sisters. He was quite taken up with his choice and when it came to good night sweetheart time, decided he would like to take her home and persuaded me to take her sister.

As the saying goes: 'Two's company, three's none, four's alright if two walk on!' They lived in the village of Cowden, which was six miles south of Hornsea but, unfortunately, we lived six miles north of Hornsea. You didn't have to be a brilliant mathematician to reckon up how far the homeward journey was. As far as I was concerned it was a wild goose chase in the first place and the journey wasn't really necessary.

Sometimes in this life you have to do a friend a good turn. Not long after this the same friend was offering me a lift in his new car . . . 'One good turn deserves another'.

Going back to that evening, we eventually arrived home in the early hours of Sunday morning. Normally when you arose looking a little weary, as bright as a button father would greet you: "Good morning; joyful evenings make sorrowful mornings." Instead, on this occasion, he said: "It's a lovely morning, but it was a cowden (cold one) last night."

When you were one of a family of six, two being girls, it was amazing just how quick news travelled. Father had a great sense of humour, but was a hard task-master who would never ask you to do anything which he couldn't do himself.

The next national celebration came on Tuesday, August 14th, 1945 when, at midnight, Britain learned of the surrender of Japan. A broadcast was made by the Prime Minister, Clement Attlee. He said: "The last of our enemies is laid low."

With most of the population sleeping, celebrations were slow to start, but the constant sounding of ships' sirens and railway whistles heralded two days of national rejoicing. The Government declared a two-day holiday. The BBC broadcast throughout the night, to advise commuters to stay at home and announcements about the holiday were made at the railway stations.

51

The next day, the crowds in London were equal to the last celebrations and churches once again arranged special services of thanksgiving. Street parties in every provincial city and town in the country had been prepared and massive bonfires burnt from every vantage point in the land.

On V.J. night, a farm pupil and myself cycled the 13 miles to Bridlington to join in the celebrations. These were even more spectacular than those held some three months previously on V.E. night. This was only two weeks short of six years since the commencement of the war, so there was every reason for people to let off steam, by dancing and making merry till the early hours of the morning.

The reality next day was not so joyful. Mr. Attlee's grim message was: "With peace comes greater austerity, instead of plenty. Britain is in serious financial trouble as a result of the abrupt ending of lend lease by the United States government. There will now have to be major cuts in imports of food, cotton, tobacco and petrol. Goods produced for home consumption will have to be exported instead and food stocks held for consumption by American forces will be eaten by British people."

Although this was bad news for the country, it did encourage the farming community to keep investing and go for maximum production. For the harvest of 1946 Irish labour was crossed off the list and the Governor hired a ten-foot cut Massey Harris combine as the replacement. This gave us an insight into the potential of combining cereals.

The following year a new Allis Chalmers trailer combine, with a five-foot cut, was purchased at a cost of £520. It was towed by a tractor and driven by a small Allis Chalmers model B engine, which was mounted on the machine.

It was unable to cope with threshing wheat, as there was too much straw to get through the machine. Wheat varieties at the time were very long in straw and there were no means of shortening them. Therefore, the only crop it could cope with was barley and we combined 70 acres of it that year.

It was a bigger combine with a chute on to drop the bags on the ground; thus we ended up with 16-stone bags of barley laid around the field, instead of hundreds of barley sheaves to gather up. At the time, we thought that this was marvellous!

It was then decided that the small Allis Chalmers combine should be sold as it had not the capacity to deal with the wheat crop on the farm. It was sold to a local farmer in 1947 for £500. This meant that only £20 had been lost on the machine and it was obvious we needed a larger machine in the future.

For the following harvest a Massey Harris 21 combine was purchased for £1,300. It was a self-propelled ten-foot cut, driven by a six-cylinder Chrysler petrol engine. The combine was imported from Canada as there wasn't any being manufactured in this country at the time.

It was fitted with a pick-up reel, which was a recent attachment. This lifted laid crops from the ground to above the level of the cutting blades, so there was no corn left uncut as had previously been the case with the ordinary type of sail. It also acted as the sails as well, to push the top of the crop towards the cutting knife. The corn then fell onto three moving canvases, one from each side feeding a central one, which delivered it to the threshing drum.

There were 200 grease nipples and the petrol tank was situated under the driver's seat. Safety inspectors had not been invented at the time, but the makers did advise to check the manifold every two hours, to make sure no straw had collected on it. When you were sitting on a time bomb, you did not need to be told to carry a fire extinguisher and take every possible precaution; you could say that 'your life was in your own hands'.

This combine had a similar capacity to the original threshing machine, but had to be more compact for practical purposes. It was no longer required to separate the chaff from the pulls, so, along with the straw, they all could go in a direct line from the front of the machine and be deposited out at the back on to the ground. This enabled the drum sieves and the straw walkers to be reduced in size.

There was also an advantage with the combined crop going into the drum much more evenly, than it was possible to hand feed the threshing machine. All this helped to reduce the size and the weight of the combine, making it a moveable working machine.

The stripper and the combine harvester were first used in the 1890s in North America and Australia. The stripper took the ears of grain, leaving the stalks. The combine replaced the reaper binder. The early types were drawn by up to 50 horses and driven by steam power, before eventually tractors and self-drive took over.

The world-renowned Canadian firm of Massey Harris built a stripper in 1896 which was drawn by six oxen. It is ironic that the stripper system was tried again in Britain in the 1970s, but never made any impact on the market and never threatened the well-established method of combining, which had been in use since the Second World War.

When we first used the combine, neighbouring farmers came to see the machine working and I was told what a good farmer the Governor was, but this would break him. We should have no decent straw for bedding, no caff for feeding livestock and were putting all weed seed back in the ground to grow again. The grain would be too wet to store, unlike America where it dried in the field before combining.

At the time, when I thought about what they were saying, there were no sprays to deal with weeds, no dryers to dry the grain and straw and caff were quite valuable products. I had to admit it didn't sound such a bad argument.

There were two people required on the combine: one was the driver and the other the bagger. The grain went into sacks, which had to be securely tied and placed down the chute. When three sacks were full, a lever was pulled and released them on to the ground.

Each night after a day's combining, all the sacks had to be stood over-end in case of rain. The sacks acted as a sheet, but if it did rain later all the sacks had to be tipped over so the bottom of the sack would dry. If this was not done, the damp grain at the bottom would sprout and be wasted.

Most of the grain would be loaded later, straight on to the lorries in the field. Two men would go with a hicking stick. This was made from a broken fork shaft as it only needed to be two foot long. You got hold of the mouth of the sack leant it over and hicked it on to the lorry.

This was very hard work and the sacks had to be filled to capacity to keep the sack hire charges down and would often average 19 stone a sack. It went to the merchant's premises to be dried and the farmers were paid on the dry weight of the grain, less drying and transport costs.

In the seven years that this combine was on the farm, it never had a new bearing or any moving part replaced. In fact, it only had one problem — a cog operated by an electric switch, which was fitted to the table to control its up and down movement. The mechanics of the system was a strong chain, which revolved round a cast cog wheel to get this movement and also to keep the table at the required height.

On two occasions this cog wheel cracked and broke. Manchester was the nearest place to get a replacement. As with all machinery, it never breaks in the shed — only when being used — and it was a four- hour journey to go and get a replacement. A combine stood in the middle of harvest for this amount of time was not acceptable.

The Morley establishment came to the rescue. As I have said before, they could make anything. They cast this cog in brass and there was never another breakage. I bet there wasn't another combine in this country with a brass cog fitted on it.

Chapter Eight

THERE were always important events happening throughout one's life, but if asked the question which qualified to be number one, it would have to be at a dance at the Spa Royal Hall at Bridlington. An ex-girlfriend introduced me to a girl called Marian. She looked stunning and was the most beautiful young lady I had ever seen in my life — but remember 'beauty is in the eye of the beholder', or we would all have been chasing the same one.

Don't get me wrong; there was opposition, as there always is when you want something desperately in this life. I have been in touch with that young lady from that day until this: I think they call it love.

When the news leaked to father, as it always did, he introduced a new signature tune. He found another song with the girl's name in it. This one went: "Mary Ann she's after me, full of love she seems to be."

In June, 1949, Low Bonwick Farm came up for sale. The Governor had been the tenant for the last seven years and the improvements on the farm had been considerable. It was to be sold by auction at Driffield in August without vacant possession. Marian and I had decided we would marry in the Spring of the next year, so would be looking for a home.

I had saved every penny possible from leaving school at 14. I had never smoked and only had the odd half-pint of beer at the Saturday dances. The reasons for not getting involved in these bad habits were:

1) I once saw a young man dancing with a very nice young lady and being sick all over the dance floor. I swore then that would never happen to me and it never did.

2) By the time I'd bought the ticket to enter the dance hall, there was very little money left.

So the order of importance was ladies first, beer second and smoking a non-starter. An uncle advised me at the time that every cigarette you smoked would buy a square-yard of land. Therefore, 20 per day over a year would have paid for an acre and half. Looking at it that way, I can only conclude that a hell of a lot of land went up in smoke! By this time my savings were a £1,000 and to be thinking of buying a 320-acre farm was rather a large order.

My eldest brother, Les, was married and living on the farm. I approached him in the first instance to see if he was interested in forming a partnership with me, with a view to buying the farm. He also had a £1,000 in savings. Although he was four years older, it was more difficult for him to save, being married and having a family.

My proposal to him was to borrow money to buy the farm. We would need between five and six thousand pounds, of which we had £2,000 between us. Then to split the house, to make a home for me and my future wife; this would save the price of another house.

He agreed in principle but was concerned about, firstly, financing the project; secondly if it was feasible and, finally, the reception which we would receive from the Governor. I maintained we must go for it or we would never forgive ourselves for the rest of our lives if we didn't try. Even if we didn't make a go of it, we had tried and, in any case, we had little to lose.

A meeting was arranged with father. I was voted chief spokesman by a majority. This was unique in any case as we met him every day, but never discussed business. Our job was to get on with the work and he would do the thinking!

At the get-together I had invited Ron, a very good friend of the Governor, to be present. Ron was a forward-looking businessman, ten years younger than the Governor and we knew he would value his opinion.

The Governor agreed he would let us take over the the tenancy: this, by the way, would reduce his income by half — no small consideration for anyone. Then wait to see who bought the farm and then try and get the tenancy in our names. We pressed him, suggesting we should be organised for purchasing it if the price was right and we could raise the money.

He said: "What are you chaps going to buy it with? Where was this sort of money coming from?" We pointed out that we had £2,000 and we should have to borrow the rest. He maintained that all those who bought the land on borrowed money after the First World War went bust.

Ron then spoke up and said: "Let them have a go, Ralph; they're as keen as mustard and won't let you down." Father then agreed we could "look into the matter further to see if we could find the money."

We then approached the banks and discovered that the maximum which they would lend us was £2,000. We knew that we would need more than that, but were not surprised they wouldn't support us.

Low Bonwick Farm was jointly owned by six members of the same family and it happened that one of them was an insurance broker. This gentleman was able to find an insurance company who would lend us £4,000. We were not in a position to negotiate interest rates, but just had to accept their terms.

We now had £6,000 available, which gave us a figure of £20 an acre. This was the maximum that we could afford and if it made a penny more it would be above the price we could pay. Having got this far, we had to think about in-going valuation and working capital.

I think the Governor was beginning to like the idea of getting two sons fixed up at one go, as his ambition in life was to see his four sons farming. He did not want to be the richest man in the churchyard and always said: "Don't make money your god." Father sowed the seed and any farmer who sows a seed looks for it to grow. He suggested that he would loan us the valuation money, interest free, until we could afford to pay him back, as well as backing us at the bank for £500.

Incidentally, the valuation was £4,000. This was for sheep, suckler cows and calves, following crop and a Ford Popular car with a new engine recently fitted. There was little more that we could do at this point of time, but get on with the harvest until sale day.

The day of the sale duly came. It was a lovely day in every sense of the word, but we could not spare the time to go buying farms . . ! We had to get on with the work and the Governor would do the business.

Late that afternoon there was an influx of people who came looking round the farm. It was obvious that we had not been successful on the day and my 'lovely day' turned into disappointment. We came to the conclusion that someone else had bought the farm and had to wait until teatime, which was eight o'clock in harvest, to hear the end result.

The 320-acre farm had been withdrawn at £4,750, with a reserve figure of £6,000 on it. The person who made that last bid was invited to speak to the auctioneers to try and negotiate a price.

The Governor made that last bid and came home. I think he came home for further instructions. Well he got them, for the first time in his life! The orders were, back to Driffield to meet the auctioneers first thing the next morning, to offer them £6,000 and button the job up.

As I've already said, there were six vendors and they would not take less than a £1,000 each and we could not pay a penny more, so you could say that there were eight satisfied people.

59

Many farmers' sons over the years have said to me that they didn't get any help from their parents. I would never say that. My parents never gave us money directly, but all the help they could, after the hard years they had been through. Our task of getting into farming, without that foothold, would have almost been impossible.

Father suggested that we should use his tackle, as the existing machinery was already doing the work on both the units. The golden rules which we had learnt as kids began to apply again: 'Be thrifty and don't spend unnecessary money'. With an overdraft limit of £500 — and you could say not another bean as all our capital had gone in the purchase of land — the bank manager would take care of the spending.

April, 1950, was the most important month of my life. April 6th, 'Lady Day', was the official day my brother and I took over Low Bonwick Farm as owners and partners. April 12th I took a partner in marriage. The world was my oyster. If you want something in this life enough and you've got a passion, the impossible becomes possible.

As the saying goes: 'You'll never get the field ploughed just turning it over in your mind'. I was marrying the most beautiful young lady in the world, who was aged just 20. We all had two hands each, we had our health and happiness and a hell of a lot of borrowed money! Money is supposed to be the cause of most problems and I was hoping some of those problems would come my way. As my best man, Bill, put it 40 years later, at the celebration of our ruby wedding: "Norman, in those days, was all dash and no cash. I'll leave the next sentence for you to complete for yourselves."

The wedding day had to be on a Wednesday, which was a law in our family and was a superstition; supposedly the lucky day of the week. The saying goes: 'Monday for health, Tuesday for wealth, Wednesday the best day of all; Thursday for losses, Friday for cosses, and Saturday no day at all'.

The morning of the wedding was spent — not very romantically I must say — unblocking drains from the house ready for our return one week later. The weather that day was almost identical to April 12th, 1998; cold with snow showers, periods of sunshine and blustery winds.

So much for the weather forecasters, who predict in 40 years time that 'our weather in this country will be equal to that of Spain and France and those countries becoming desert', (so says Bill Giles).

The wedding was at Driffield Parish Church at 1.30 p.m. and the reception was held at the Rink, with the catering being done by Mrs. Kay from the Southorpe Lodge. This all passed by in a flash and the dreaded moment which had been worrying me for some time was approaching — the MC's next announcement: "The bride-groom would like to say something in reply . . . "

If you believe that you would believe anything. I did say a few words and I remember the end of that speech to this day. I had said it at least a hundred times before:

> *"Thanks to Mrs. Kay for the reception,*
> *Thanks to our parents don't come last,*
> *Thanks to you for the lovely presents,*
> *And thanks to everyone for all the past."*

Having got that off my chest, I really then began to enjoy the day. Unlike today, as soon as the reception and speeches finished, the bride and groom would go and change into their 'going away' attire and before very long either a taxi or car would pick them up and take them to a secret destination. In our case the Ford Popular was ready to take us on our journey.

Honeymoons in general don't appear to have the same meaning these days; there never seems to be any urgency to get on their way. There must be some reason for this as human nature does not change, but we older ones must not jump to conclusions.

The secret hiding place of our car had been discovered and the vehicle had been filled with confetti. This aside we set off on our way to the Station Hotel in York, where we were staying for the first night. We pulled into a lay-by along the way to clean out the car and, to this day, when we pass that spot we talk about that day. Bed-and-breakfast at that up-market hotel was the pricey sum of £1-16s.

The following morning we made an early departure for Edinburgh. We knew that we had a long day ahead of us as our car could not exceed 30 miles per hour until the new engine had been run in, otherwise there was a risk of it overheating.

The journey was not an easy one; no road signs had as yet been replaced after the war and motorways didn't exist. We stopped off for lunch for half an hour and the total journey took nine hours. Consider today, you could go via London to Edinburgh in the same amount of time.

There's no need to tell you that we both slept well that night; in fact, for the next two nights. The second night the clocks changed — all that is, except ours, so we were an hour late for breakfast. The staff took this in good part, but the embarrassment was for Marian and myself. The last thing anyone would think about on the third day of their honeymoon would be altering a clock. Well it never entered my head! We had a good week's holiday touring the area.

Neither of us had been to Scotland before, as holidays were seldom on the agenda at that time. Petrol was still on coupons, which restricted travel, but the greatest restriction was that of money. Towards the end of the week we pulled into a petrol station for some fuel. When I handed the attendant my money and coupons he said: "I don't require coupons today, sir; petrol has been taken off ration. I only need the money." So I always remember petrol rationing ended the second week in April, 1950. When we landed back home and told the tale of our nine-hour journey, the quip was, how many gateways had we pulled into on our way north!

Chapter Nine

S O, arriving back in Yorkshire, I went to live on the third farm of my life along with my wife. Unlike many young couples who go into the farming business and spend money on their house and contents, we realised this would be money laid dead. Bricks and mortar seldom make money and certainly don't make a happy home. It's the people inside that count and, as the saying goes: 'Love in a cottage is better than hell in a castle'.

This new home, like the one which my mother faced in 1928, was no 'des. res.', nor had it any mod. cons. The toilet at the bottom of the garden was something else; there was no need for an extractor fan as the air flowed freely on its own! There was a bench with a hole in it, which you sat on, and also another hole in the back wall which enabled you (sorry me) to rake the contents into the ash pit. So the ash pit served two purposes.

I had been the sanitary inspector at home, so you could say that I was qualified. Back at home the toilet had a bucket, which needed emptying, so you just dug a hole tipped in the contents and buried it. At least there wasn't a dirty big hole in the back wall to serve as an air vent. Needless to say my first job was to update the toilet facilities. This meant blocking up the hole in the back wall, redesigning the seating arrangements, introducing a toilet bucket and making a moveable front to get the bucket out.

The water supply was from an outdoor pump, with a copper being used to boil water for washing. Our kitchen was converted from a horse's stable, the floor was concreted to level it and a kitchen fire range put in for cooking purposes. The brick walls were left as they were as funds were not available to plaster them. Living quarters were the kitchen, one room and two bedrooms. Shared accommodation was a dairy, an entrance hall, the staircase and an outside wash-house.

Where would you find two wives who would put up with these conditions for over four years, in the modernised world of today?

I have always said that getting married is the biggest gamble that anyone takes in their life, but borrowing £4,000 with only £2,000 worth of assets come a very close second!

So it was nose to the grindstone, with 16 hours a day being a normal day's work on the farm. After tea — 'for leisure' — we concreted buildings out, mixing the cement by hand, with lanterns for lights. It was essential to get some livestock enterprises started to bring in weekly cash to pay the wages.

We needed £13 10s. 0d. a week in order to pay ourselves and one man. We decided to install battery cages for 500 hens and a 20-sow unit to produce weaner pigs. None of this could be done until we got the concrete laid. Time was of the essence; the sooner this work was completed the sooner we were in business.

There was no electricity or mains water supply to the farm; all water for livestock had to be led from the pond with horse and water cart. In due time we got both these utilities established and though only small by present day standards, they contributed to help the business on in those early days.

Battery hens when culled after a year's egg production were worth up to a £1 each and would weigh in at about seven pounds each. In those early days, we were interested in the Landrace breed of pigs. One of the few breeders in the country was based at Settrington, near Malton. We went to try and buy a gilt in pig and the asking price was £300! With overdraft facilities of £500 to run the whole business, there was no way we could raise the funds.

We were very disappointed as we could see the future in Landrace pigs. We did, however, muster enough money to buy a Landrace boar, which we used for crossing on our Large White female line. The weaners we produced soon became worth a premium over our other pigs, so the little extra price of the boar was soon written off.

On 17th March, 1951, the birth of a baby daughter Christine, was to make this a very exciting year in our lives. Marian was 21 and I was 23, which was quite young by any standard. Unlike many couples in this age group, who tend to lay the foundations for a home or business before having their family, we decided to start a family while we were young and bring them up along with building our castle.

This seemed to us to be a better way, for while work was going to be the major priority in our lives, bringing up a family could become the leisure part of it. Time and money were both in short supply for any other leisure activities. Everything had to be ploughed back into the business if we were going to survive and at the time there was no guarantee of this.

The next major job and expenditure on the farm was to install a mains water supply. The nearest point was at Dunnington and this was a mile away. Fortunately it was across our own land and we got permission for the go-ahead almost straight away. This, of course, was at our own expense.

The pipes were ten feet long and two inches in diameter. They were made of asbestos with collars and rubber washers, and three nuts bolted them together to seal the joints. This meant that every ten foot per mile, there were three bolts to tighten! We hired a small mechanical digger which was driven by the power drive on a tractor and, on a good day, we would complete about 20 yards.

It took us a year to do the job and this was in early 1952. There have been no leaks in that mile of pipeline to this day, which is 46 years ago. I still wonder about this asbestos pipeline from a safety point of view as I know of no other such pipeline and, if a leak did occur, there would be no way it could be repaired.

From living in the backwoods we thought heaven had come to us when turning on a tap and clean water poured forth, both for livestock and household use. This also enabled me, as sanitary inspector, to modernise and further improve toilet facilities as well as do away with the tin bath. In other words, a bathroom and water toilets were installed. The only other mod. con. not yet available was electricity, but as they say: 'Rome wasn't built in a day' and 'Money doesn't grow on trees'.

February 3rd, 1953, hurricane winds combined with high tides brought disaster to the East Coast of Britain. Sea defences collapsed from Lincolnshire in the north to Kent in the south — 280 people were drowned and thousands left homeless. Damage was estimated into hundreds of millions of pounds.

Clacton holiday chalets were under 12 ft. of water. Twelve American servicemen were drowned near Hunstanton. This tragedy came hard on the heels of the January storms in Scotland, which destroyed trees worth more than £3m.

In 1953 the Ministry sanctioned an importation of pure-bred Landrace pigs from Denmark. The sale was held at Peterborough: there were 40 lots consisting of three gilts and one boar per lot. This was unique; never before had the pig world experienced anything like it. Top price was in the £5,000 region, with very few below £4,000. To compare the price in relationship to land prices at the time . . . a local 190-acre farm made £9,000, the price of eight pigs. Today you would need in the region of 9,000 bacon pigs to buy that farm.

To say we should have moved heaven and earth to have found the cash for that £300 gilt in 1951 was an understatement. It did, however, double the price of our cross bred gilts and everything looking like a Landrace had a price on its head. At least it proved our thinking to get into the breed was the right one.

We probably should have tried to borrow the money from the bank, but there always seemed to be another project up front needing the money, so it was a matter of selecting the most important. First priority was to pay the valuation and clear our debt with the Governor. This was only right when we were making money and he was receiving no interest on money lent to us.

We were all happy as sandpipers, cruising along in our own sweet way, spending money on the bare essentials, when we got a shock in the form of a tax demand. This was to be the best business lesson we ever had in our 20 years partnership.

We were having to pay what in those days was known as super tax, which amounted to 60 pence in the pound. We had very little of our own machinery, a reasonable valuation and very little borrowed money as far as working capital was concerned.

There was only one way to counteract such a tax demand: the name of the game was to expand the business. This meant more borrowed money, so it was back to see the bank manager and into the sweat box once again. We had electricity installed, paid our valuation off in full, bought a new Massey Harris combine, mechanised our farm to a reasonable level and reluctantly paid our tax bill.

We were all brought up to never grumble about income tax. The Governor farmed 15 years without making any profit and said that he would have been very pleased over that period to have been paying some! You cannot argue with the fact: you only pay tax when you've made a profit and you cannot expand unless you are doing just that.

In the Spring of 1954 we heard of an old gentleman of 86, who was considering retiring from farming. By this time there were four children and four adults living in the one house. I knew from farming experience that when stocking rates get too high, troubles are not far behind!

Nobody had said anything, nor was there a hint of any upset, but we could not expect our wives, who were both working very hard to help us, to continue family life sharing a home much longer. For Les and I it was a different story. We got the change of scenery each morning. There was still plenty of work to be done to keep us out of mischief, no problem there; but that was not the same as being confined to one house bringing up two families.

The farm, which the old gentleman had lived on since 1892, was called Southfield Farm, Skipsea. He had been farm foreman there for 32 years and tenant farmer for the next 30 years. This was the very farmhouse I had seen and admired as a schoolboy cycling to school.

I thought this was a good chance to add another 105 acres of land, near our present unit, with no extra labour or machinery needed. Most important of all it would provide a much-needed second home, which was only fair to both our wives, who had put up willingly with less than ideal conditions to help us to establish a farming business.

We found out who was the owner of the farm and I made an appointment to go and see the man. He was a Driffield landowner and a real character. I knocked on the door, introduced myself and mentioned that I had heard his tenant at Skipsea was retiring. For a guess he was a man in his sixties; I was 27 and had always been taught to respect my elders, which is not always helpful when trying to do business.

He replied to my question: "Well, the knows more than I does, lad." This stopped me dead in my tracks, but then he softened up a little and invited me into his home. Whether he began to view me as a potential customer, or admire me for my damn cheek, I'll never know.

A generation gap of this magnitude takes a bit of bridging, but I liked the old gentleman and got the feeling he was beginning to take to me. Confidence began to return to me, so I asked him that if the farm did become vacant would he give me the first chance to rent it? He said he could not promise that, for he might decide to sell it.

At that point I forgot all about the bank manager and stuck my neck out and asked him for the first chance anyway. He said: "I will, lad, and let you know if I hear anything." You could say I'd got one foot in the door; which was very important and is always a good start.

Two months later he wrote to me, telling me his tenant had given notice to quit and he had decided to sell the farm. We had been hoping the farm would have been to let, for we knew we should be pushing the boat out again as far as borrowing money from the bank was concerned. I still thought this was wonderful news. We were in direct contact with the owner, no auctioneers or estate agents involved. We had first chance as the owner had promised at the beginning. I wrote for permission to view and duly received it.

I invited the Governor to come and look round the farm with us and give us his opinion. He was not very impressed and thought it was a poor farm. No way would he have considered buying it and thought if we did we would be making a grave mistake.

We knew in the first place he was not a land buyer, and a quarter of the farm was grade three land anyway and therefore not suitable for arable cropping. In fact, seven acres had been flooded by the sea in the 1953 floods and had a three-year gypsum allowance. The gypsum had to be spread on the land to counteract the salt in the soil, until some sort of plant life started to grow. This was expected to be for about three years, but until it happened there was no point in sowing any crop, not even grass.

To put it in a nutshell, everything on the unit including the house and toilets could only improve; well, they couldn't get any worse. We were considering buying a farm, which was not unlike the one my parents rented in 1928. The potential of the land was not quite so good, it was once again no 'des. res.' and there were no mod. cons. but, beggars can't be choosers. As far as I was concerned the green light was at 'go'.

The next move was an appointment with our bank manager: we were about to enter the sweat-box again. He was a bowler-hatted character: actually he didn't wear it at his desk, but in his temperament he always had it on. There were no such things as cash flows; you either talked yourself into him lending you the money for the project or talked yourself out of it!

I seemed to be doing all the talking and when I'd finished putting our case forward he put his elbows on the desk, making a V shape and said: "You boys build your castles like this." Then reversing the position, said: "Instead of like this" Δ. "You really need a bigger base before you do anymore expanding."

I pointed out that an opportunity like this very often only comes once; it was a chance in a lifetime to do a deal like this. We had not talked money up to now; it was a matter of crossing the bridges as you came to them. He did appear to be showing a little more interest, so I mentioned the sort of price we had in mind.

We thought about £75 an acre, making a total of £8,000 and this would be our top bid. There would be no more labour costs or machinery needed. After a few 'ums' and 'ers', he eventually agreed in principle to this amount. We left yet another meeting feeling quite pleased with ourselves and the final result.

We would have our final inspection to note all the faults and also all the good points. Needless to say it was about ten-to-one in favour of faults! The two or three good points gave us a strong enough case to go ahead with the purchase.

I made an appointment with the owner. He was asking £8,000 for the 105-acre farm which I told him — with all the faults it had — was far too much money. I battled away for two hours, not upsetting him in any way and his final figure was £7,800. I came away with my expectations fulfilled and I had got the price down by £200 in two hours. That was the first time in my life that I had earned a £100 an hour!

*Above: Skipsea School,
1937. Norman is top right.*

Left: aged 18 months

Top: Spellow Farm.
Above: Low
Bonwick (1950).
Right (centre):
Aged 18, outside
Manor Farm,
Dunnington.
Right: Southfield
House, Skipsea.

Norman's father ('The Governor') and mother on their golden wedding day.

Below: Mr. and Mrs. T. Warkup, The Mill, Beeford, with Albert Widdas, Maud Walker, Albert Walker, William Warkup and Mr. Jerry Walker.

*Above: Tom Warkup
(Miller Tom).*

*Right: Oliver and
Hal Morley, Beeford
Blacksmiths.*

*Right: Norman (far right),
brother Les (centre) and
Charlie Bibby.*

*Left: Geoff Riby
(far left),
Norman's
partner at
Sawkill, with
Colonel Starkey.*

*Phil Tuplin
(left) and
Phil Woodcock
(right).*

v

*A two-row
bobbin drill.*

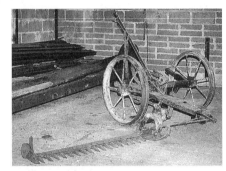

A grass reaper.

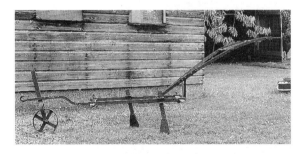

A scruffler.

*A Ransome
three-furrow
tractor plough.*

(Photos courtesy of
Bill Scrivener).

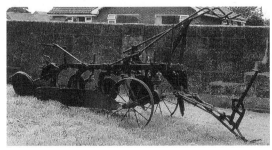

Wedding day,
April 12th,
1950.

The Kirkwood family — Norman and his wife, Marian, with their
three daughters: Gwen (left), Caroline (centre) and Christine (right).
Inset — Ruby Wedding (top row): Charlie Byass, Caroline, Christine,
Will Waind, Tim Lansdell; (front): Gwen, Norman and Marian.

Left: Norman with Shire horses in the paddock.

Below: the dream bungalow.

Three grandchildren — Philip, Emily and Peter.

Chapter Ten

IN August, 1954, I went to live on the fourth farm in my life, together with my wife. This was our first home, the home we had longed for since the day that we were married. It was no palace; in fact, it was not much better than a chicken hut, although it was much bigger and had the potential of making a nice house.

As an old gentleman once advised me: "It's better to take a new young wife to live in a chicken hut, than to take her to live with the family." This applied to both families; it was only fair for each family to have their own home — thus avoiding any rows which would certainly have happened in time and ruined a good partnership with a lot of potential.

Having lived at Southfield Farm for just over a year, on the 15th November, 1955, Gwendolyn, our second baby daughter, was born. This again was a red letter day. She was the first baby to have been born at Southfield for over 60 years and children had never been seen playing on the lawn throughout that period.

The farm land ran down to the sea, so we had a private beach. The following summer the beach was at our disposal and it was free entertainment for a baby and a five-year-old. At the time, with tight purse strings, it was the only type we were likely to get. It was seldom anyone was seen on this stretch of beach and we nearly always had it to ourselves.

The East Coast has miles of golden sand and excellent beaches, but it seems we have been born a few hundred years too early, as the boffins predict a climate similar to France and Spain will eventually arrive here. At present, the wind is mostly easterly off the sea and bathing days are few and far between, but the children still liked the sea.

Expansion in small steps on a regular basis was a safe way of moving forward. Our bank manager didn't see it this way. He thought the steps were too regular and much too steep, but bank managers don't have to be good business men. Give them credit though; in those early days they would stand by you and take greater risks than is possible today.

The borrower also took risks. If he went bankrupt he couldn't sue the bank manager for lending him too much money. Today's manager is in a precarious position. If I were able to bring a new law into this country, this situation would be reversed: as I see it 'You can't have your cake and eat it'. Any solicitor or lawyer who sued a bank for lending too much money, would be sent packing to jail. This would give young people a better chance to start at the bottom and get into business and be able to borrow money from the banks to do it. The bank would also have more liberty to help the likes of me as they did in the Fifties.

Although the house was very old-fashioned, it was an excellent building of some substance and quite large. The kitchen was 36 feet long, 15 feet wide and 11 feet high, with a beamed ceiling. It had a massive black-leaded fireplace with a side oven and hot water boiler, which were all heated by the kitchen fire and had a kettle hanging over it.

To the other side was what was known as a sheet or bread oven. This was very large but heated by another fire directly beneath it. The mantelpiece was seven feet high and there was a screen round the fireplace to try and make a warm, secluded area.

Nothing in this house had been altered for 62 years. There was a paraffin lamp for light and the old gentleman used to sit behind the screen. This was more like a scene from Dickens than a place to take a young wife and a three-year-old daughter to live, but as I have said many times before: 'It's the people who make the home, not the bricks and mortar'.

There was a low but large dairy at the north end of the kitchen with staff sleeping quarters above it, which made this corner of the house three storeys high. All windows, both upstairs and down, on the east side of the house were fitted with iron rods, which were one inch in diameter and spaced nine inch apart. These rods had been put in when the house was built.

From the inside of the house it was like a monkey's cage and from the outside like a prison. This was not in case of burglary, but so the workers could not get into the house after closing time. The doors would be locked at 9.00 p.m. on weekdays and 9.30 p.m. at weekends. Not only would the staff who were locked out have to find somewhere to sleep in the farm buildings; they would be severely reprimanded for not being in on time.

There was a back door on the east side of the kitchen, into the backyard and also a door on the south side directly into the farm building. This was not a very satisfactory method of keeping vermin out of the house but the only way to the toilet. There was an entrance hall, with two rooms, one each side of the hall. Like the kitchen, all the rooms in the house were high. There was no electricity but water was laid on into the yard. We had only had electric six weeks at Low Bonwick after which we were back to lamps and candles; so much for progress!

When the old gentleman moved out he only took with him the furniture and utensils that he required for his new home, so this meant that the house was half full of his unwanted possessions. We had many hours of entertainment emptying that house. We took a truck load of junk and dumped it into the pit. It wasn't until 30 years later that we realised our mistake of disposing of hundreds of pounds worth of valuable goods.

Visiting the toilet reminded me of Goldilocks and the Three

73

Bears. There was a bench seat at the back of the building. A third of the bench was set at half the height of the rest. There was a large round hole in the first section, presumably for father, a medium hole in the second section for mother, and a teeny weeny hole in the lower section, so baby didn't drop straight into the pan.

You can just imagine at six o'clock each evening, father saying: "Before we lock up, shall we all take a walk to the bottom of the garden." If it was not intended to use the facilities together, why put them there? I always maintain families should do things together; there should be no going your own way. You should go out as a family . . . but I thought this was taking it a bit too far!

I did say that things could only get better and I have listed quite a number of faults. As you will have gathered by now, toilets seem to be my speciality, so as piped water was available the first thing on my list was to install a bathroom and water toilets. No more going to the bottom of the garden.

Most toilets didn't have a lock on the door; well, the one at Skipsea was no exception. Why have a lock on the door when you were all in there together? The tale goes that the old gentleman had a business acquaintance visit him. When he was about to leave he asked permission to use the toilets. The old man pointed to the door at the bottom of the garden. When the visitor returned he mentioned the fact that the toilets didn't have a lock on. The reply came: "I've never lost a pan before."

The next job was to block the doorway leading from the kitchen into the outside buildings, thus making the house vermin proof. Then there were the iron rods to remove from the windows. I wondered why they hadn't been confiscated for arms during the war, as this would have saved us a hell of a lot of work. This action immediately turned the prison-come-monkey-house-look into a very smart red brick house.

Out came 'the beautiful large cooking range' as described by the last tenant. Black lead had gone out of fashion! The mantelpiece was lowered, so that we could reach the clock to wind it up. Then we spent eight hours upon scaffolding, scrubbing and washing the ceiling. This was the beginning to make the chicken hut more like living accommodation. Then over the next few years we decorated the rooms and painted the exterior, according to time and money. A house in my view needs a complete renovation once every 30 years; this one certainly needed two!

The poor end of the farm ran half a mile down to the coast and was three fields wide. Sea erosion was taking on average one and a half yards per year. The best side of the scenario was it was taking the worst of the land, but the worst side was it was taking land that we had paid for, so the size of the farm was decreasing. Investing money into land was a good business, but losing a percentage each year was going to take the icing off the cake. So this was another good reason for only looking at this farm on a short term basis.

The sea had always been an attraction to Marian and myself, so living by the seaside was a pleasant part of our lives. To have half a mile of private beach, where we could go and have a swim or take a stroll on a weekend or any evening, with not a soul in sight, was something out of this world. The sound of the waves and the peaceful atmosphere was one thing which money couldn't buy.

The greatest disadvantage of this coast line was continuous easterly winds. If only we could have ordered a westerly wind on a permanent basis, this would have been paradise and ranked one of the best beaches in the country, having literally miles of golden sand.

Having got the house all decorated, a bathroom and water toilets and electricity installed, in this our first home, we had become very attached. The thought of moving on in the future was something that neither of us could apprehend or looked forward to. Yet we both knew if the opportunity arose it would have to be done, to climb another step up the ladder!

75

The in-going valuation was as follows: the total fertiliser used over the whole farm the previous year was 30 cwt. of phosphate. One would have expected this to be at least six times more than that. There was one shire horse, one ram, one sheepdog, 30 ewes, six beasts and 20 hens. This was a real *Macdonald's Farm,* not very much, but a little of everything. I don't remember the price of the valuation, so it couldn't have been a breaking matter.

This farm was unique in many ways. For someone to have lived there 62 years: lost his only daughter at the age of 60 and she was the last baby to have been born on the farm. There had been two periods of prosperity and two depressions during this time, which will not happen to many individual farmers in a lifetime.

At the time there were ten farms in the village of Skipsea and this was the only farm not in milk production. However, today it is the only one producing milk and this is the ideal job for this particular farm.

From the word go, we only looked at Southfield Farm as a stepping stone, as 105 acres with quite a lot of grade-three land was not my idea of a farm for the future. It was too small for a single arable unit, for when the day came to dissolve the partnership, as we knew it would, it would not be able to support a family. This was yet another farm crying out to be treated like a baby. "It had not been kept clean, its body not well nourished and its bottom not dry; it was clean it up, nourish its body and dry its bottom."

Hedges and dykes were attended to and drains in wet holes were taken up and cleaned out. There was a seven-acre field, which was very good land, but very wet and needed draining. We put tenders out for this work and three old hands who drained for a living came up with the best price. They were more competitive than hiring drainage machinery.

When the work was completed and paid for, this seven acres was still below the £100 an acre mark. Although the tasks to improve the farm, with the mechanisation taking over in general from hand work, it was beginning to make much of what we had been taught in the Forties become redundant, as many of the jobs did not exist any more. There was one thing we had learnt in the early days, which still applied: this was to work hard and be thrifty.

We specialised the livestock enterprises on each of the farms. The battery hens, breeding sheep, the 30-sow herd breeding weaners and the 18-month beef fattening enterprise, were all carried out at Low Bonwick. At Southfield we concentrated on rearing calves to supply cattle for grazing the leys on the 18-month system at Bonwick.

We had a herd of 15 breeding cows to put to a Hereford bull and each suckled four calves — the calves having been housed in loose boxes or buildings on the farm. The cows were brought in twice a day to suckle them. We always put the cow's own calf to a foster mother; this way the cows accepted the four strange calves much quicker.

The name of the game was to get the cow to take the calves — this made the job much easier, as until she did you had to tend the suckling — making sure all the calves got fed and none got kicked off, which would have meant them going hungry.

Initially, each cow had to be supervised twice a day, so there was a lot of time spent getting the cows to foster their calves. Some would take to them in two weeks and others would be two months.

We also bought in another batch of two- week-old calves and bucket-fed them. They were fed twice a day for six weeks, by which time they were eating solids and were then weaned. This meant we had somewhere in the region of 80 cattle to go to graze grass on Low Bonwick Farm, so the two units were becoming integrated, one relying on the other and making use of all facilities available.

The summer of 1955 was a very good one, both from the point of view of the weather and cereal yields. The best possible thing to follow expansion was a good dry harvest and as you were expanding all the time, it helped if you had one every year!

Half of our cereal acreage was being combined and the other half still being harvested the old-fashioned way. We were young men and wanting to modernise, but were restricted to how much we could combine, as storage and drying facilities were not available. The same old problem was facing us once again. As soon as you got an idea in your head it costs money and it seemed to be the only commodity that was short in supply, but at least work never was. As the saying goes:. 'Live as though you're going to die tomorrow and farm as though you're going to live forever'.

The following year was the last year for us to use the old-fashioned method of harvesting. The reaper binder was sold for £30, which was a good price at the time. The whole farming system was to move on. No more stooking, leading, stacking, or threshing sheaves. This meant more skilled jobs going by the wayside, particularly the stacking, which very few people were able to do. The threshing machine pulled out of our stackyard for the last time, much to my pleasure: another job I hated was crossed of my list for ever.

This brought an entirely new system to our farming. A new bin-drying and storing building was built in reinforced concrete blocks, with our new bank manager's blessing! There were ten bins each 10 feet square and 16 feet deep, holding 32 tons per bin, thus giving a storage capacity of 320 tons.

The grain pit was at the end of the building, where the grain trailers tipped their load. It then went directly into a 12-ton-an-hour elevator which, in turn, fed the top conveyor. This took the grain to the bottom of each bin, which allowed the grain to flow by gravity into the bottom conveyor, to be taken back to the elevator for loading. Each bin had a ventilated floor with individually controllable air ducts; this enabled any or all the bins to be dried at one time.

A coke fire was installed to heat the air and would use a hundredweight of coke per day. A fan, driven by a large diesel engine, was used to blow the warm air down the ducts into the required bin or bins. Although by this time we had electricity, we had not the horsepower capable of driving the fan, so had no alternative but to power it by diesel engine. The complete cost of the unit was £6,000, which was £18 per ton stored.

We were fortunate with the choice of contractor who installed the drying equipment, in as much as he had been dealing with the drying and storing of grain over the previous 20 years for the likes of Ranks and the big millers in the city of Hull. His knowledge, experience and advice had not been available to the farming community at the time.

This was one of his first ventures into on farm drying and storing of grain. Technically he knew the amount of heat required in relation to air flow through the grain and also the depth of the grain in the bin, which also came into the equation. He recommended to always put a ventilated floor in a building for grain storage purpose, as you then had the ability to blow air through at a minute's notice, if the grain was not keeping satisfactory.

We had updated our system for the start of the 1957 harvest. Not only had the sheaves disappeared for ever, but the 19-st. sacks of grain which were dispersed all over the field had not to be man-handled any more, for they had also gone. All the grain now would be moved in bulk on both the farms.

This alone took a tremendous amount of hard work out of harvesting. Once the grain was in the bin on the ventilated floors, the drying process was continuous day and night unmanned. Unlike the through dryers, where grain was moving all the time, they needed staff in attendance all the time.

Less movement of grain cut down the cost of production and labour force was also reduced, as it only then required two men to do the harvesting — one man driving the combine and the other carting the grain to the drying unit. Doing the whole job on the farm gave us more control over keeping the grain in good condition and also marketing the grain, which was very important as most of it was grown for seed and required special attention.

Up until this time, harvesting had finished at six o'clock on a Saturday night, after working long hours. Sunday, truly, was a day of rest. Now the men were both riding and the job was much easier, the week was extended to seven days; this was another way of increasing output. There was also another reason for doing this. The grain was now being left in the field until it was ripe and the risk of loss was much greater than the old-fashioned way of harvesting, where the sheaves were put into stooks to dry and ripen and there was no fear of it being shattered, as in the case of standing cereals.

All straw behind the combine had to be baled for livestock use. This was done with a pick-up baler, with a sledge behind, leaving eight bales in a block for automatic loading. These were lifted on to trailers with a fore-end loader, fitted to the front of a tractor, to deliver to the stackyard. They were then forked on to an elevator, which took them on to the stack.

One good fit man was still needed to stack these bales. The only hard part of this new system that continued to exist. These small bales, the only ones at the time, ran into thousands on the two farms, and when stacking each individual bale was handled by the stacker.

We completed the 1957 harvest in record time without any complication and feeling the full benefit of our updated system. The next year's harvest was also a good one and again we were pleased with the way things went, for expansion was afoot again, but we needed more than our fair share of luck to achieve the next step up the ladder.

Chapter Eleven

S PELLOW FARM, Elmswell, Driffield, was advertised to let. It was a 309-acre farm at the foot of the Yorkshire Wolds. I always said, throughout my life, if I ever got the chance to farm at the foot of the Wolds, I would move on to higher ground, without any qualms about leaving Holderness.

Les and I made it our business to visit the agent to get permission to view the farm. We were very impressed with him and he was very helpful and said he would forward us the particulars as soon as they were available. In due course he sent us them, with permission to inspect the farm, and invited us back to see him when we had been round the farm and farmhouse.

The 1958 harvest on the farm had been completed, so all the growing crops had been harvested. This proved unfortunate as there were hidden problems we discovered the following Spring. We walked the farm, weighing up the pros and cons, and decided it could be made into a useful and productive farm. We knew that there was a lot of hard work to be done, but this was nothing fresh, so we would set our stall out to go for it tooth and nail.

The first thing that impressed us was there were no dykes on the farm and no land drainage. The water not only flowed down to Holderness, the country we would be leaving; it went there free of charge! This would be quite a new experience for us — getting rid of water; for on the land we were farming it was a very expensive but necessary exercise to farm such land efficiently.

There was a good depth of soil on the whole farm, similar to Holderness, and the prospect looked good, but there was plenty of room for improvement, as there was on many more farms at that time. The farm rose from 50 to 200 feet above sea level; the lower land being quite heavy but becoming lighter on the rise, but still not typical Wold land and looked like growing wheat better than barley.

There was a private road, a mile long and in very bad condition, which served two farms. About a quarter of a mile had not been repaired for 17 years, as there had been a dispute between the two tenants as to whom it belonged. The landlord had solved his problem and given it to the new tenant of Spellow Farm. Not only would they acquire a bad road, but also get extra non-productive land, added to the acreage to pay rent on, with no dilapidation allowed.

The farmhouse was yet another disaster area. Although water and electricity had been installed by this time, they were the only plus factors in the equation.

Another visit to the bank manager to inform him of our intention. We explained that we would sell Southfield Farm to help raise some capital, but would need higher overdraft facilities with the increase in the acreage, and the house would need capital spending on it.

He agreed to support the project, so we were in a position to apply for the tenancy. Once a decision like this has been made you've got to pull all the stops out, so we made another appointment with the land agent in order to glean as much information as was possible and also lay our cards on the table. We had just one trump card in our hand, in as much as if we got the tenancy of the farm; Southfield would have to be sold.

I've no need to tell you the name of the auctioneers who would be selling the farm! There were two good reasons for this. First and foremost, in my opinion, we didn't stand a cat in hell's chance, without offering a carrot and, secondly, we needed the capital to make it a viable proposition. While we were there the agent divulged a guide line for the rent. Not too high and not too low. I suggested a figure: he didn't say yes and he didn't say no. So we had to draw our own conclusions; but we left the meeting feeling that it hadn't been a waste of time and the journey had really been necessary.

We then applied for the farm and had to nominate two referees. We chose a well-known and well-respected retired bank manager from the city and one of the leading farmers in our area. Both agreed to act on our behalf if required to do so. We were told there would be a short list of six applicants who would be called for an interview and, more than likely, the landlord would inspect your own farm if you were already farming.

Time passed by and we heard nothing, but knew of farmers who had been contacted to be interviewed on the due date. We assumed that our first application for a rented farm had failed. That was until one day when I was due to attend a funeral in the afternoon of a lady teacher who had taught me at school in my early days.

That morning I received a telephone call from the agent, requesting I attend a meeting that afternoon at his Hull office at two o'clock and "if you are still interested in Spellow Farm, you'd better be there. This will be your one and only chance: the ball's in your court."

I said: "My brother and I will be there." I made arrangements for someone to represent me at the funeral and Les and I made our way to Hull for the appointment. The meeting went better than either of us had dreamed, and the landlord asked if he and his agent could view our farms. This thrilled us both beyond belief and was much more than we had expected. We arranged for them to come for lunch and then tour both our farms.

On the said day, the agent and the landlord arrived; we had lunch and then went round both farms. They seemed to be very impressed with what they saw. When they had departed, I said to Les that I'd got a feeling we'd pulled it off, but he was not so sure and I could see by his face he was thinking that I was a bit of a big head; but only time would tell. A week later we got confirmation we were the new joint tenants of Spellow Farm.

The rent was set at £4-7s. per acre, with the option of a 43 acres permanent pasture in addition to the farm at £4-10s. per acre. This made the farm 352 acres in total. We just couldn't believe our luck. We knew there were a great many applicants for the farm. So, we assumed our bid was not too high, nor yet too low.

The next assignment was to organise the sale of the 105-acre Southfield Farm at Skipsea, obviously with the said agent. Farmers came and looked round the farm; they viewed the house and everything in it. A few were interested and a few were not, which is usual when selling a farm.

The day of the sale arrived. The auction was held in their saleroom in Hull. I was at the sale on my own and, when the bidding started, I was devastated. I had never felt like this before in my life, and never since, for that matter. The farm was sold and realised £900 more than we had purchased it for — four and a half years earlier.

We had sold our house, the place Marian had made into a beautiful home. It had become her roots and it broke her heart and she wept for days at the thought of leaving it. My feeling was like being stood on a cliff edge wondering if I'd jumped the right way or not. Up until then a brick wall wouldn't have stopped me once my heart was set. Now I was not so sure; my confidence had diminished somewhat.

However, in my mind it still seemed the right move for the future, as the day would come when the partnership would have to be dissolved. A small farm like this, with grade-three land, was not the kind I had in mind for spending the rest of our lives on. I promised Marian the dungeon at Spellow would be made into just as nice a home as the one we were leaving and reminded her it was the two of us and our family who would make it a happy home, not the bricks and mortar.

The landlord was not prepared to spend any money, neither on the farm or on the house, but willing for us to alter the house with their approval. To be honest, there was nothing to approve: apart from knocking it down we couldn't have made it any worse. There was only one room in the house, which did not need attention. It was the upstairs' bathroom, which came complete with a water toilet. This was the first home we had moved to where my sanitary skills were not required! The modernisation had already been done.

On entering the house you walked into a back kitchen. Immediately to your left was a door into an enclosed staircase, which led to the servants' sleeping quarters. In the far right hand corner was a built in copper, so in effect, this was also the wash house. Another doorway straight ahead from the back door went into quite a large kitchen, but this was about four yards shorter than the one we were leaving.

There was a door out of this kitchen down the centre of the house into a very dark passage. On the left-hand side were two dairies: one of these dairies had been used for salting bacon in brine. Shallow enamel troughs stretched all the way around the walls, with just a walk way down the middle.

Above this flat-roofed dairy was an outside concrete water tank holding thousands of gallons of water, collected from the whole roof of the house. This water would have been used for washing purposes only, as there was an outside pump and well for drinking water. On the other side of the passage there were another three dairies, the first one opening into the kitchen and the only one in use. At the end of the passage was a doorway to the right directly into the dining room. In the far left-hand corner of this room was a door which opened on to the front staircase.

There was yet another door directly across the front of the

staircase leading to a sitting room: this staircase was also enclosed between the two rooms. It was noticeable, when we looked round the house, that the telephone was situated in this far-off sitting room, which made one wonder how many calls they just missed! Planning officers must not have existed then, but even today some of their decisions, in my experience, are not much better.

Our job now was to redesign the house to our specification and make a nice, workable home. Both the existing staircases were removed. The old copper was done away with, and the back kitchen was to be modernised to become our new kitchen. An Aga cooker was installed and kitchen units with sink and storage cupboard put in place. The old brick floor was taken up and replaced with tiles.

The doorway into what had been the kitchen became a serving hatch, with the old kitchen making a large dining room. The passageway left from where the staircase was, gave us a doorway through on to the central passage of the house. Another doorway was made out of this kitchen in the near left-hand corner, directly into the first dairy on the left, which would now be used as our dairy.

The next step was to make the two dairies on the right-hand side into an entrance hall, with a new staircase leading onto the landing. This did away with the central wall down the right-hand side of the dark passage, and also a wall dividing the two dairies. The two existing dairy windows were left in place, and a glass doorway put between them make it now a very pleasant west-facing entrance. A new maple floor replaced the old brick one, completing the attraction.

The third dairy on the right was made into a shower room. Removing the front staircase made this into a spacious sitting room and did away with the two original doors across the front of the staircase. The brine dairy became the office, with the corner taken off to make a doorway and entrance into what was the sitting room: this became the television room. The telephone was duly moved into the entrance hall, which, as the Governor would have said, was using your head to save your feet. There were alterations upstairs, but not to the same degree as had been required on the ground floor.

While all this work was being carried out, we had the good fortune to be invited by our parents to stay with them and commute to the farm each day. I had promised Marian we would not move into the house until the work had been completed, as we had lived amongst the chaos twice before in our lives.

When we moved into our new home, this was the fifth farm in my life and the one I have been farming ever since. I was reminded that 'a rolling stone gathers no moss' but, I had learnt as a young man, that you sometimes have to roll it a little in this life to get in the position you want to be!

On the farm there was also plenty of work to be done. There was Spring barley to be sown and all this land had to be ploughed. A 20-acre field had to be worked and planted with potatoes. Cattle were brought on to the permanent pasture to graze and sheep on to the white clover, which the previous tenant had sown. When the barley got established it was undersown with grass seed, using a fiddle drill, for as yet there had been no progress in this department.

One morning, when going to inspect the Spring barley, I got rather a shock with one acre of the field, as it looked as if it had been sown with oats! These were, of course, wild oats — a weed that was common in Holderness but unheard of on the Yorkshire Wolds.

I had bought in all new certified seed barley, from a reputable company to sow the farm, so it was obvious that wild oat seed was in the ground. They were affecting 36 acres in a 56-acre field very badly. In the other 20 acres there were quite a few, but it was possible to rogue these out.

I immediately rang the agent and informed him of the problem, requesting that he and the landlord visit the farm to see for themselves. They came the very next day to inspect the field, but couldn't understand what all the fuss was about. When I explained it was a weed and would take at least eight years to rid the farm of it, the landlord made it quite clear it was not his problem, nor would he make any allowance for it.

I mentioned before that when we looked round the farm, the harvest had finished as we had no idea the weed was present, but understood the situation. I only wanted to point the problem out to him to prove the responsibility for bringing this unwanted weed on to his farm was not mine.

There were no sprays available to control the weed and our idea was to grow corn for seed on this farm. So the weed had to be removed as quickly as possible, but at least retained in the field. The only way to do this was to crop it out; this meant no cereals on the 36 acres for eight years.

The reason for this was the plant must not be allowed to seed for that period of time, otherwise the control would not have worked and would have been a waste of time. To achieve this, the cropping schedule was three years grass ley, then one year roots. This was then repeated, giving us the eight- year period we required to do the job. Unfortunately, this meant that we were unable to grow wheat on this land until 1968.

Two weeks before the 1959 crops were ready to harvest an in-going valuation had to be done. Each party engaged an auctioneer valuer to work on his behalf. The depth of the foldyard manure had to be measured to determine the amount of cubic yards there was in the foldyard. There was a fixed price per cubic yard and then the cash value would have to be agreed.

A proportion of artificial manure used over the last three years would be taken on an annual basis from the invoices, and a cash value put on them. Following wheat crops, which the outgoing tenant had sown, had also got to be valued. The two valuers were taken in a horse-drawn cart, through the growing crops, to estimate the output.

The driver was instructed to drive to any part of the field, which either of the valuers wanted to see. The exercise made me cringe: to see a horse and cart trampling down standing corn was beyond belief and looked a 'Heath Robinson' way of doing what could have been a simple job. Two men in a cart estimating the yield of a growing crop of corn was like gambling whether the coin was going to fall heads or tails.

I have always maintained throughout my farming career that there is enough gambling in the farming business, without risking extra money on things which could be determined in a more accurate way.

The luck was with us once again. As I have mentioned before, a good harvest in the first year of a new venture was essential, not only from the cash point of view, but it also gives you a moral boost for the future. We had a record harvest as far as grain output was concerned, and the glorious harvest weather that year enabled us to combine all our grain without a break, and the corn was sold not needing any artificial drying. This was fortunate as there were no drying facilities on the farm, so if the season had not been a good one, the drying would have had to have been done on contract.

We had to take one step backwards at this point and bag all our grain from chutes on the back end of our grain trailers. This meant we were back to the hard work again; man-handling 18-stone sacks of wheat. At least this quickly made us make up our minds to take steps before the next harvest; to have a new drying and storage system installed. This was to be similar to our original one, but not a purpose-built one. It was Crittall bins erected under an existing Dutch barn. Being tenants, this gave us an efficient unit at half the cost, which one had always to have in mind.

Ten 32-ton Crittall bins with underground air ducts were put in, with a large 40-horsepower electric motor to drive the fan, to blow warm air through the grain. This was heated by a coke furnace which, incidentally, used one and a half hundred weight of coke per 24 hours. At the time it was the most economic way to dry the corn we could find.

We approached the next harvest with our new plant all in place and ready to go. We noted a few wild oats round the headlands of the fields. These we assumed had been carried there by the combine from the badly infested field. After the machine had combined it, then moved into the next field, always starting round the headlands, a few wild oat seeds would obviously be left in the combine and this was the cause of the problem. Again, the density was not so great and it was possible to hand-rogue them out. We were already growing corn for seed purposes, so decided to expand this on our new farm.

There are three main weeds which will not be tolerated when growing seed corn. They are wild oats, cleavers and runch (wild radish). This means all seed crops must be hand-rogued to the required standard. They are examined twice in the growing season by a qualified, independent inspector, to see if they meet the standard for a pass. There was a good premium for good quality seed and we looked on this to put a little extra jam on our bread!

Seed growing, however, created more work and extra costs. Many hours were taken up walking the fields and each lot of seed when combined had to be segregated, so more storage room was required. We looked on seed growing as a discipline to keep our farms in good heart and clear of all weeds. No matter how few weeds there were, every field was walked; our philosophy was we would walk a mile if only to pull one wild oat.

Break crops consisted of a small acreage of potatoes and the rest was two-year leys. Silage was made for both cattle and sheep.

The farm was low in phosphate and potash, with the heavy land short of lime. There were many farms in the same situation and, as the Governor pointed out, it took him ten years to pull round 'home' farm. In his opinion, the answer was to increase livestock on the farm and this would help to get the humus content of the land higher, with grazing and the manure they produced.

The rotation to achieve this was a third of the farm in break crops, chiefly two-year leys, but 15 to 20 acres of potatoes were included in this. A third winter wheat and a third in Spring barley.

A flock of 200 Suffolk cross-breeding ewes, put to pure bred Suffolk tups, became the sheep enterprise. An 18-month beef system was introduced, fattening 150 beasts a year, primarily off grass with a little rolled barley towards the end of the fattening period. This improved the land in the shortest possible time.

Chapter Twelve

ARCH, 1961, Caroline, another baby girl was born; more joy but no boy! So we had three daughters spread over ten years, or one every five years. I was told at the time, elephants produce their progeny every seven years, but it was moving farms, which seemed to spur us on, as our family increased by one each time we moved to another farm.

As farmers breeding stock, we were well aware of not always getting the sex you were looking for, but the lesson was that, as long as mother and off-spring were fine and in good health, the sex was of very little importance and there might be a chance next time.

In our case, we decided bringing three girls up and being in the farming business was as much as we could manage. There was to be no more increasing, but spreading our family like this meant we were visiting the seaside over many years; but, most importantly of all to us, was family life and we always went out as a family.

We also started a small turkey unit, fattening 500 birds in the first year, for the fresh Christmas market. This put us in touch with Raymond Twiddle, who was in business breeding turkeys. He invited us to join him, form a company and build a factory, to produce oven-ready pre-packed birds, initially for the Christmas market. Another producer had also been approached and the company was formed and we became shareholders of a third of Twydale Turkeys Limited.

A pack-house was built and the three parties produced fat turkeys to be processed through the factory throughout the whole of the year. A system with a conveyor line was installed. The birds started at the beginning by being stunned and slaughtered, then finished at the end, frozen and packed in individual boxes, ready for the market.

After being slaughtered, they were put on the conveyor line; they were then scalded and went through a plucking machine. Any remaining quills or feathers were removed by hand, and they were then drawn and made oven-ready.

The next step was to take them off the line and put them into cooling tanks, where they stayed for eight hours. The work was on-going, but done in two stages. After eight hours, they were taken out of the cooling tanks and put into plastic bags. A machine sucked all the air out of the bag and sealed it up, making it waterproof. The bag was then put into a liquid brine for a given period to freeze the birds, and finally they were put into boxes marked with our company name. The boxes then went into cold store ready for the market and were sold throughout the country.

We had diversified into the turkey industry . . . 'taking our products to the housewife', just as the Governor had advised us many years before. In the first year we processed 20,000 turkeys and the cost of freezing and packing was 14 pence per pound weight.

The next year we doubled the output throughout the factory. This was achieved by incorporating outside producers to rear on contract a proportion of the production requirements. This was an interesting exercise: by doubling the numbers through the packing house it brought the cost of freezing and packing down to seven pence a pound weight, just half the cost of the previous year.

This was a lesson in our business lives we never forgot. If to co-operate means to reduce your costs by half, you can't afford not to do it. Turkey numbers reared on Spellow Farm went to 20,000 a year and the other partners were doing similar numbers, plus the outside producers. This took the numbers to 100,000 a year by

1966, which was maximum capacity possible for the factory and machinery to cope with.

A big expansion was planned to buy a large building and put the necessary equipment in and to eventually take the numbers processed up to one million. We were asked to partially back this project, but thought it not wise to take such a risk; so we decided to dissolve the partnership and leave, taking our shares out of the company.

The turkey-rearing buildings enabled us to start a broiler breeding unit, supplying hatching eggs for Ross poultry company on contract. Four thousand laying hens were housed and we were soon in production. The eggs were collected from the farm weekly.

The turkey poll barns were adapted into barley beef sheds and numbers were built up, to average ten seven-cwt. fat beasts to market each week. The manure from this influx into livestock, particularly the turkeys manure, which all went on to the grass leys, altered the farm beyond recognition. Along with more modern techniques, which were beginning to come through, the increase in yield was quite good.

We had also become involved with I.C.I. and each individual enterprise on both farms was being costed: thus we were being kept informed of many advances in their own farm trials. There were no charges for these services, but we were expected to purchase our fertiliser requirements from the company.

They visited each farm once a month for all information, and it was processed through a computer even down to private drawings. This gave us valuable data on our accounts, but most importantly of all, gave us the accurate cost of production, which very few farmers knew at the time.

It is always essential to know the cost of production to be able to market your commodities in an efficient way, and it helps to determine the best time to sell them. At the time, I.C.I. were doing experiments in all fields of farming, but particularly in grassland production and utilisation.

They introduced us to a new system to fatten lambs — known as forward creep grazing. The field was split up into six paddocks. The ewes and lambs were put into a paddock with a creep in the fence; this allowed the lambs to go forward on to worm-free fresh new grass, so they were always on the best grazing.

The ewes were made to clean up after the lambs, before they were moved forward. That particular paddock was subsequently top dressed with nitrogen: this not only increased stocking rate three-fold, but also enabled us to market our lambs in less time. The grasses received 300 units of nitrogen per acre and 4-cwt. of silage per season was being taken off the leys, plus any excess on the lamb paddocks.

This was pushing our system to the limit. In fact, one season in the mid-Sixties when we had five inches of rain in the month of May, with two inches in 24 hours, our lamb paddocks became 'paddy fields', and the whole flock had to be moved on to permanent pasture. A third of our silage leys had been cut and left to wilt for 24 hours: this was on a first year ley, so the ground was very tender.

The grass lay there for two weeks, with no chance of us being able to pick it up. In the end we had no option but to move in and pick it up, as the grass under the swath was deteriorating rapidly; in doing so we acquired another 'paddy field'. This proved to us that we had pushed the boat too far: in fact, a boat would not have been out of place!

We had learnt the lesson once again. Mother nature will only let one go so far before she puts her foot down, and that rule still applies today. The costings proved that wheat was the most profitable crop on the farm and the sheep the least, even at a high stocking density.

The time had come when a more business-like approach had to be taken in farming. No longer could we afford to have an enterprise just for the 'manurable' value. Each one had to pay its own way, or there had to be changes. In my mind the land was too good for farming a low output venture like grazing sheep, so they had to be sold. This allowed an increase in the wheat acreage on the farm and also increased profits!

The livestock left on the farm was barley beef, 18-month grass-fed beasts and broiler breeding hens. The next year, profits from barley beef were beginning to disappear, so no more rearing calves were bought in. This meant over a period of nine months, barley beef would cease to be produced.

Barley beef in this area were still being marketed in large numbers. There were at least 20 farms rearing and fattening over 500 head of beast per year, and this was putting pressure on the market and lowering prices. So yet another livestock enterprise disappeared from Spellow Farm.

1969 was another eventful year in my career, with quite a few changes occurring and moves in different directions. The next thing to bite the dust was the broiler breeding unit. This, initially, was very profitable, but after four years began to tail off. The potential was needed to create a more profitable venture. Being a producer for a large company was not my idea of a past-time. Not only did the time pass by, but most of the money passed by with it! . . . so we went solo once again.

The buildings were then converted into a 200 sow-breeding unit, through to bacon. This, with the 18-month beef unit, gave us a good balance of profitable livestock. Times were demanding more specialisation; larger units, and pigs were also noted for being good improvers of arable land.

One of the buildings was converted into four separate farrowing houses, with nine crates in each house. They had a covered forward creep and laying area for the piglets which was heated with a lamp, this attracted them into that area.

The next building became a dry sow house, with four rows of sow stalls, holding a total of 90 dry sows. We designed our own individual sow feeders. These were filled by hand to enable us to give the correct amount of food to each sow. At the end of the row of sows was a lever which, when released, fed all the sows at the same time. This reduced stress on the sows by all being fed together and the feeders were then refilled for the next time of feeding.

Down the side of the building there were eight boar pens, which acted as the serving area as well as housing the boars. Another building was utilised for putting sows in after they had been tested and certified in-pig. These were also in stalls and on automatic individual feeders, this was a mechanised system as all the sows were being fed a standard amount of food.

The final building, the largest one at 180 by 42 feet, became the fattening house and held 900 pigs through to bacon weight. An additional flat deck house was built for weaner pigs. These were weaned at three weeks old. The floors were cast-iron slats, so the pigs were never in contact with dung. It was a controlled environment building, but split into individual sections. The reason for this was if an outbreak of any virus took place, it was less likely to spread to all the pigs in the building.

This turned out to be a profitable project and I swore then that I would never again in my life be involved with birds . . . that is those which have feathers on!

At this point of time, Les and I decided to dissolve the farming partnership. He had a son and two daughters and I had three daughters, so another generation was becoming involved. We'd had 20 happy and successful years working together, and had in effect, two established businesses, so it was quite straight-forward to do the split. He became the sole owner of Low Bonwick and I became the tenant of Spellow Farm, with Marian a business partner.

There are advantages and disadvantages in both these positions. The big drawback of a tenancy is the restriction of being able to just get on and do your own thing; whereas, as an owner-occupier, you are able to get on without any interference. I realised that not having any capital in land meant expansion was a major priority in one form or another. As the saying goes . . . 'as one door closes another one opens'.

Chapter Thirteen

I WAS now looking for that opening. By chance I met Geoff Riby, who had just finished at Bishop Burton Agricultural College. He mentioned he was looking for a job managing a cow unit. Having no contacts with anyone in the milk industry meant I was not in a very good position to help him in that way. However, it had crossed my mind before this, that a cow unit might be a good investment, as we were buying two-week-old calves for our beef unit, so this would be killing two birds with one stone.

I was always interested in breeding any stock, but milking cows was not my scene. I asked Geoff if he would be interested in setting up a cow unit as a junior partner with me. He was delighted and said he liked the idea. I had first met Geoff as a choir boy at the local church. He impressed me as being a rum lad and always had a smile on his face. As I have said before, I've always taken to rum lads; they never stick fast in their lives and will always go places.

Geoff's family had the misfortune of losing touch with farming through a tragic accident and losing their father. I'd seen him working amongst cows on a local farm where he was well respected. He then went to Bishop Burton College for two years' study, then another year out on practical work, before going back to college to do a year's management course.

Throughout this time he had shown great promise as a stockman. He won the first Lionel du Pré award for the student of the year.

How much more was needed to prove to me he was the right choice for a working partner?

The next and most important part of the procedure was to find a farm . . . 'Just like that' as Tommy Cooper, the comedian, used to say. There were very few farms coming on the market to let at the time, so the type of farm and the distance had to be flexible. It was no good looking or waiting for an adjoining farm; this would have taken years. We only had months. We viewed two very poor wet farms in the Howden area which were 30 miles from home. We applied for both without success. The motto was: 'If at first you don't succeed, try, try and try again'.

The third farm to come on to the market was Sawkill Farm, Huttons Ambo, near Malton, which was some 20 miles away. Yet again we applied for particulars and permission to view. The reply stated it was by appointment only and viewing was to take place on two days only and they wanted to know which day we would prefer.

We chose the second day, hoping it would be the least popular one and that fewer people would be viewing then. We were then informed there were many applicants for the farm and we were given a time for the appointment. This was no surprise to us: with so few farms coming on to the market to let, there was bound to be many interested farmers looking for expansion.

The day came and we duly arrived at the farm gate to find a fine, tall elderly gentleman with a moustache and a figure as straight as a pole, accompanied by another well-dressed gentleman — not quite so significant but nevertheless very polite. We really were amazed and wondered . . . had we come to the right place?

Mine hosts were the colonel and his agent, who said that they wanted a word with us before we ventured any further. They advised us there was a tractor with a farm trailer taking a load of would-be tenants round the farm, but that it would return for the next load in half an hour.

They went on to ask many questions about our intentions if we were the successful applicants. It seemed unusual to them that someone already in arable farming, was going to form a partnership with a 20-year-old who was just leaving college, and was not even a relative. They made it clear the farm would only be let to one person by name, but did not rule out it being farmed by partners. They didn't seem to be interested in me becoming the tenant as I was already tenant on a farm, and most tenancy agreements state the tenant must live in the farmhouse on the farm.

The next problem was Geoff not being of age to become a tenant on the farm, as you were required to be 21 years old. At this point we let it be known we had no milking cows, so would have to start a new herd if we were to become the tenants. Although there did seem to be many questions to be solved, the colonel did invite us to meet them at the farmhouse after we had viewed the farm.

We made the decision to walk the farm, just the two of us. My idea of viewing a farm from a trailer was just not on, but to be joined on that trailer with the opposition was beyond my belief. I always walked my own farm for two reasons: one to keep me fit and the other that you are more likely to see any problems from a pair of boots, than you are from any vehicle.

So Geoff and I set off on our walk round the farm, the only pair to do this as far as we could see. We were able to take notes and discuss matters on our way round, something none of the riders would be in a position to do.

It was April, 1969. This was a very wet heavy land farm, with 190 acres all being grass. The 108 cow herd had been out-wintered on the grassland and it was badly patched. The damage was extensive to the point where grass was going to be very scarce for the coming grazing season, and cattle feed would have to be purchased throughout the summer months. As one would expect from these conditions, the cows were in a poor state but were well-bred cows from the Terling and Lavenham herds in Essex, and these would be the type of cow we would be looking for. Again this was

101

a farm which could only improve: there was no room for a backward step, neither with the farm, nor the condition of the cows.

We thought that it had potential and were aware there was a lot of improvements to be made before it would be in full production. Drainage and re-seeding the farm would be the major priority, but would have to be spread over three or four seasons.

Before returning back to the farmhouse to meet the learned gentlemen, we made a decision to go for it, although it wasn't the most desirable farm: we had to accept the fact that 'beggars can't be choosers'. We knew it was a hard task and would have to be started on a shoe-string. Geoff's capital was similar to the amount I had started with in 1950. The total capital to get this enterprise started was £13,000.

> *The bottom is the place to start*
> *To climb the ladder in this life,*
> *And if by chance you miss a step*
> *A fall will bring you strife.*
>
> *N.E.K.*

In our summing up it occurred to us that they hadn't made a very good job of the timing of their sale. The farm was to let from the 6th October, 1969, but the cow sale was to be held on the 31st July. We realised then we had a trump card up our sleeve and could make it work to our advantage.

Having finished viewing the farm and buildings we made our way back to the farmhouse. We viewed the house before meeting the landlord and his agent. In the ensuing discussion we pointed out that we should be looking to buy at least a third of the dairy herd at the sale on the 31st July . . . This would not only improve his sale, us buying these cows, but we should also be bidding for cows throughout the sale, thus pushing the prices up across the whole herd. We then pointed out that should we buy the cows that day we wouldn't have anywhere to milk them until the following October.

I saw the colonel's moustache twitch; his eyes were half smiling.

I knew he had taken the bait; we were half way there. He then asked if we would be prepared to take the farm over the day after the sale if he decided to let it to us. We said we would be pleased to work on those lines.

On leaving the farm that day we felt pretty confident of our chances of being offered it, therefore achieving our aim. This made our day's work very rewarding, but we had been told that there were another 86 applicants, and so there was still some thought and work to be done.

We received a further form requesting full details of our farming experience and our financial situation. They made it clear they thought that a partnership was a good balance; a young man to manage the farm and build up a good dairy herd, with a little farming experience in the background. It was ironic they should mention a young man to manage the farm, as this was the only commodity missing when they were farming it themselves! They were also suggesting ways of getting round the problem of Geoff being too young to be the tenant, so things were still looking promising.

An offer in writing had to be made for the rent of the farm. We had thought about ten pounds per acre, but seeing he was a pedigree Friesian man who always worked in guineas, we made it ten guineas per acre (or 21 shillings). This was sent off with fingers crossed, to arrive before the closing date, when a short list was to be made and successful applicants notified within the following week. This was a long week, but luck was on our side once again and we had been placed on the list.

We had seemed to be in the driving seat most of the time, but nothing was happening very quickly. They were beginning to test our endurance. Was someone going to pip us at the post? After all, like a race there can only be one winner. D-day finally arrived and in typical army fashion we were lined up and then called in one by one (two in our case).

The interview went very well and they seemed to be asking all the right questions for us to answer. At the end of the interview the landlord made it quite clear we were the sort of farmers they had been looking for, but didn't say so in as many words. He told us we would be notified by post as to the result within the next week. A few days later we received a letter. Geoff and I had become the proud farmers of Sawkill Farm, Huttons Ambo. We had become partners and dairy farmers overnight for the first time in our lives.

I have seen so many father and sons in farming partnerships who just could not develop a good relationship in farming. I blamed this on the generation gap, but often wished I'd had a son to prove that this gap could be bridged.

I now had acquired a partner 20 years my junior. The challenge was now on. Could we see eye-to-eye and prove it was possible for that gap to be bridged? Obviously a young man has a different point of view at times, but there is nothing to stop an older man trying to think young and doing a bit of give-and-take in life. Right from the word go, we held meetings round a table in a business-like fashion to make decisions; something very few father and sons in farming do.

The first such meeting was to determine how we were going to operate at the forth-coming cow sale. Our aim was to set up a 120 cow unit, buying as many cows as feasible at the Sawkill sale. Our policy was to buy some of the best cows, but keep a running average of around £120 per cow on the day.

We had inspected the herd and done a serious selection. Then we crossed the bottom third off our purchasing list. This gave us a guarantee that all the cows we bought would be in the top two thirds of the herd, so some of the better cows would be above this price and the average cow below it. We were lucky in as much as at this particular time dairy farmers couldn't get out of cows quick enough, and there were more cows on the market than it could absorb.

In fact, quite a few cows on the day were purchased for slaughter, even from a good pedigree herd like this. Once again we were very pleased with our day's work. We finished the day purchasing 65 cows at an average of £118 each and were milking cows the very next day.

Not only were we milking our own cows: half the remaining cows from the sale were still on the farm, with the purchasers requesting us to milk them till they could get them moved. There was as much milk in the collection tank on our first day in dairying as there was on the last day of the previous owners, and the name of the game was to fill that tank.

We were still looking to increase cow numbers and were fortunate once again, for two months later another large herd of pedigree Friesian cows came for sale. The Barmston herd, which had some excellent cows in the catalogue, gave us a golden opportunity to increase our numbers.

We were to use the same strategy as we had done at the previous sale, only selecting stock from the top two thirds of the herd. Remember, these were the days before quotas had been invented so it was just a matter of purchasing the cows.

On arriving at the farm on the day of the sale, we were amazed at the lack of interest and the small number of buyers in attendance. This was evidence once again that milking cows was not in fashion and demand was very poor. From the point of view of the dairy farmers who had spent all their lives in the trade and were about to retire, this must have been the worst possible time to have made that decision. As was expected, the cows were very cheap on the day. We bought 51 cows, at an average price of £118 each.

This gave us a herd of 116 cows and they had cost us a total of £13,680. Our capital had been spent and we were well and truly on borrowed overdraft now!

Interest rates in the 1970s are worth noting. The year 1970 started with a rate of 8%, with a reduction to 7½% on March 14th and a drop to 7% on April 15th. By the end of 1971 they were down to 4½%. At the end of 1979 they were at 17%.

The policy right from the start was to upgrade the herd. Any cows not pulling their weight or not up to our standard were culled and replaced by better stock. The cull cows were more often than not making more money than we had paid for them in the first instance. Good bulls were always used to try and increase both output, and butter fats. Semen was also purchased from some of the best bulls in the country.

By 1972 there had been a big improvement in the standard of grazing on the farm. Buildings had been converted into loose housing, having individual stalls with automatic feeders at the front of each one. A silage system was also introduced with the idea of producing cheap milk from the grass leys.

We had nowhere near consolidated our position in the dairy industry, when we received a telephone call from our landlord, the Colonel, requesting us to meet him at his office in two hours time; once again this, as usual, in typical army fashion. We arrived not knowing what this was all about, and were surprised when he offered us a 300-acre arable unit to rent.

An opportunity like that only happens once in a lifetime. We agreed to look into the matter and would take it on providing we got the backing of our bank manager. It was obvious in our situation we needed his approval.

What an important man he always seemed to be; but there was no way forward without his help. You can imagine his face when we put this project to him! It was a good 300-acre arable unit with a 15-year tenancy, at £9-10s. per acre.

After the initial shock and a little gentle persuasion he accepted. We had no alternative but to go ahead with the arrangement. So another increase in overdraft facilities had to be negotiated — this seemed to be becoming a regular occurrence in my life. The advice I always got was to 'consolidate before further expansion', but 'there is no time like the present' and 'you seldom get two bites at one cherry in this life!'

It would have been possible to have made more money investing capital into other schemes, rather that a cow unit or any other farming enterprise for that matter, but money is not the be-all and end-all in this life.

Geoff and I shared some memorable times going round the country buying both good cows and bulls to improve our herd, meeting people in the Friesian world, improving buildings and land on the farms . . . these experiences were something that money could not buy and made our work a tremendous pleasure, which I believe no other industry is able to enjoy.

In 1972 yet more expansion was in the offering in the future at Spellow Farm. The East Riding Quality Bacon Producers Association Group came up with the idea of forming a central milling site to serve all members of the pig group. It was clear at the time a number of the group's members were at the stage of reviewing their milling facilities, and were having difficulty in choosing the size of machine they would be needing for their requirements for the future.

Pelleting feed at the time was in the minds of many of these producers, but was a very expensive operation on an individual basis. It was agreed by the majority of the group, that the Agricultural Development Advisory Service should be asked to do a feasibility study, into the possibility of establishing a central milling complex for the members of the group. The report was favourable, so it was decided to engage an accountant who had experience in such matters to do a detailed study for the group.

A very good report came back which gave us enough confidence to make a decision to go ahead with the idea. When it came to capital requirements and tonnage to be taken up by the group, some members, as was expected, did not want to commit themselves to that extent. So this meant to get the project off the ground, they would invite known pig producers to join the scheme and there were soon 23 names of pig farmers with the 15,000 tonnage required committed to the idea.

At the time, co-operative enterprises of this kind were being encouraged by successive governments. Grants were obtainable from sources set aside for industrial expansion, and also a grant from the EEC Central Agricultural Fund was awarded. Thus the co-operative milling project had sufficient committed farmers, a clear policy, a scheme, and the necessary financial support to set the ball rolling. A site at Cranswick, near Driffield, was developed, the mill was built and production commenced on the 21st October, 1975.

The first requirement as far as pig feed was concerned was for a high-nutrient/high-density diet, with the manufacturing system aimed at the lowest possible cost. All transport was to be done by local contractor, and everything both in and out was moved in bulk. This was most probably the first mill in the country to be thus designed.

Only pig feed was to be manufactured and there was a limit to the number of feeds to be produced. This in itself would mean less stocks of ingredients, less stocks of compounded foods, and less time lost in changing diets to produce different pellet sizes. In the second year the tonnage sold was 18,000, due mainly to non-shareholders purchasing feed from the mill. This proved it was a good quality product at a reasonable price.

Cranswick Mill Limited was set up to do just that and also make a profit in its own right — unlike many other farming co-ops which were only interested in paying all profits back to shareholders in dividends. This not only discouraged outside purchasers from dealing with the said companies; it also created stagnation within that company, as there is no such thing as standing still in a business. It is either moving forward or going backwards and very few of them survived in the long term.

Cranswick Mill started in a very small way with £96,000 of farmers' capital and eventually went on to the stock market and became a private limited company. The 1998 accounts showed a five million pound profit, with a considerable number of shares being held by large city investment consortiums.

Chapter Fourteen

THE decade of the Seventies proved to be one of many changes. On February 15th, 1971, after centuries of dealing in pounds, shillings and pence, Britain changed to decimal currency. So 1s. meaning one old 'shilling', which was also known as a bob, became five new pence; 'p' replaced 'd' for pence and the old half crown was now 12.5 pence!

The chief worry when this system was introduced was that traders would tend to round prices up, making goods more expensive. The politicians assured us this would not happen but, in fact, this was the case immediately after the change; the increase in inflation was tremendous.

Tractor fuel prices went up from £98.50 for 500 gallons, in 1970 to £345 by 1980. Rents in the same period went from £6 per acre to £25 per acre. These sort of increases were general across the whole spectrum of farming — machinery, fertilisers, sprays and labour, all were included.

Land prices, vacant possession, also went up from £300 per acre to £1,800 per acre, which was the obvious cause of the rent increase which took place. House prices also went along with this trend; the effect was that owners of land or property became much wealthier, but with no more liquid cash available.

The couple who had bought a country cottage for a few hundred pounds, now had one worth thousands and those who had put money into the purchase of land had improved their financial situation. Not only that, but it also enabled them to borrow more money for expansion on the strength of their position.

This was probably the first time for many years when inflation, particularly of land and property, was making much more money than actually farming the land. This did not apply to the tenant farmer, but fortunately for all farmers of this country, technology was beginning to go in leaps and bounds. There were sprays coming along to control weeds and diseases in all crops. The plant breeders were developing new and better varieties of seed, and the more timely use of nitrogen fertilisers were all helping to improve yields by dramatic steps.

Over the ten-year period wheat yields went from two tons per acre up to three and a half tons per acre; this was the greatest increase in cereal output of all times.

These were remarkable changes to take place in that era, when one takes into consideration that rent on our own farm went from £4-7s. an acre in 1959 to £6 an acre in 1970. This was only a rise of £1-13s. over a period of eleven years, giving one some idea how static prices had been previously.

However, by 1984 the magical figure of four tons per acre, or ten tons per hectare as it had now become known, had been achieved by many farmers — particularly on the good wheat growing land of this country. This was the equivalent to breaking the sound barrier in the world of aviation!

The average yield on our own farm, including barley, topped this figure. It must be recorded this was the most outstanding harvest in my 34 years in farming. I, like many more in the farming world, thought the four-ton crop had become a regular occurrence and would be the norm in the future, but as happens in many cases when growing crops, Mother Nature has her say and these sort of yields were difficult to maintain.

In July, 1973, I formed a partnership and went into the garage trade. This was with two brothers both involved in the trade and I had had dealings with the companies they had worked for. One worked for a firm of agricultural machinery dealers and was an excellent mechanic, capable of running such a company. The other brother was head salesman for a large company selling cars and was noted for his expertise at the job.

I'd often suggested to them that they should start up in business on their own as they were an ideal couple to form a workforce to run a garage business — one to look after the spares and repairs and the other to manage the sales side of the business.

A well-known garage came up for sale in the town as the owner was retiring. It was what I called a tired business, as most of the farms I'd been involved with had been. I approached them to see if they were interested in forming a partnership with me as I thought they had the potential to swing such a business, as it needed two young men just like them to get it off the ground and going again.

It was left to them to consider the project and get in touch with me if they thought any more about it. They were not long making their minds up; that they would have a go if I would be involved in an advisory capacity.

We first looked at the property that was quite a good site in a good situation. We then looked at the figures of the previous owner, which were not very encouraging, and realised there was some thought and work to be done before we approached the bank manager.

With their thoughts and quite a lot of anticipation we put a case together what in our minds was possible to achieve. Sales of new cars we put a target of 50 in the first year, plus a similar number of second-hand ones. The spares and repairs of the business had to be much better than in the past, but they were confident some of their previous customers would follow them into their new venture.

The next move was a visit to the 'sweat shop'. The bank manager went through those figures with a fine tooth comb, hesitated and then said: "You haven't got a cat in hell's chance of hoisting this flag with these figures.

111

The two lads were astounded at his comments: their faces dropped when they thought their fairytale had come to an end. As the saying goes: 'There are more ways than one to skin a cat'. I'd always maintained in my business life that if a bank manager ever said no to me and would not lend the money, he would never get the chance again and only one ever did.

My reply to him was: "If you don't do this business today, someone else will get the chance tomorrow." This gave him one of two choices; he had to either lose a regular customer or support the proposition we had put forward. He decided to back the project. But when now does a bank manager give his support to this extent?

It is impossible for me to accept the latest idea of being able to sue the banks for lending too much money. This has made the banks very reluctant to take the risk of lending money to young men, on the basis they think they have the potential of making the grade and starting up their own business, but are short of capital and have not got necessary collateral to cover the borrowing.

If this had been the case in the early days of my career, I would never have been able to start in business. Even though we had to borrow from an insurance company to start, we still needed the bank manager to finance our business and he would not have been in a position to lend money to what the total assets added up to. So today this has become a problem, finding the necessary capital, and has a detrimental effect for the young man starting at the very bottom.

The garage business took off right from the start and continued to do very well. In fact, in the first year the projected cash-flow figures we had presented to the bank were double, something which has never happened to me in my farming life! It continued to expand over the next four years to become a very profitable enterprise.

At this point of time the partners suggested buying me out. We agreed terms and, after enjoying four years in the garage trade, it made farming with only one turnover per year look a bit of a second-rate undertaking! It is most important to dissolve such a partnership while all the partners are on speaking terms, otherwise it can become a very expensive exercise.

In 1974 Marian and I took a cruise on the QE2 to see if we liked the sea life. Following this trial, in the following year, we splashed out in style and celebrated our Silver Wedding anniversary on a holiday cruise around the Caribbean Islands.

After lunch on Christmas Day, 1978, whilst sitting round the dining room table, the girls and their future came under discussion. Both mum and I put our cards on the table saying in fun: "You are not all staying at home." Little did we think that Gwen would leave by marrying Charles Byass on August 1st, 1979, followed in ten months by Christine marrying William Waind on June 4th, 1980.

Not only did we acquire a second son-in-law but also with him came a bonus of three grand-children: Stuart, Angela and Fiona.

The Christmas conversation must have been taken seriously and I had two weddings to pay for in ten months. This did little for my cash flow! 1980 was another memorable year, for November 7th marked the arrival of our first grandchild, Peter.

In 1979 I became involved with a local accountant who owned 22 acres of land and wished to form a landlord-management partnership. It was February, the field had not been ploughed and was in a very bad state with wicks (or twitch as it is known locally) being the main weed. Fortunately the chemical spray 'Roundup' had been invented to deal with such problems. It had put an end to the expensive old-fashioned summer fallow, where no crop was grown in that season.

This spray should have been applied in the previous Autumn, as recommended by the manufacturers. This was to ensure the spray was taken up by the leaf of the wick over the winter, but that time had long since gone. This left no alternative but to apply the spray in February, leave it a couple of months for the weed to absorb it, then plough the land and take a gamble and sow it with Spring barley.

Although the barley crop was nothing to write home about, we did achieve the object of cleaning the field. This arrangement continued for three years, then the owner decided to take the land back in hand and farm it himself with contractors. This was not a very satisfactory arrangement from my point of view, as the land was now in good condition, but while involved with this project I saw the most desirable bungalow and paddock.

The first day after working the field and returning home, I said to Marian: "I have seen my dream bungalow today," but for the second time in my life it was beyond my wildest dream that I would ever live there. Fifteen years later it became our retirement home, which proves if you want something enough in this life 'the sky's the limit', so go for it; there's no telling what can be achieved!

The costings on the beef cattle over a period of time were not satisfactory and proved they were only making a profit every other year and this was just not good enough. Unlike our forefathers, who were more interested in a foldyard full of manure, regardless what the cattle in it were worth, or if they would leave any profit.

Farming had now become big business and could not afford to carry non-paying passengers. Without much effort a decision was taken to sell the cattle, making the farm an all arable unit. The pigs which were doing well at the time and were contributing to the business, were kept to produce the manure and keep the farm in good heart. After all, pigs were noted for being the quickest and best way of improving an arable farm, so you could say we were killing two birds with one stone.

The landlord was then approached to see if he would give permission to drain and plough out the old 43-acre permanent pasture. He declined, saying he wanted it to remain as parkland for conservation reasons. So, no longer having grazing cattle on the farm we surrendered the tenancy. Needless to say, two years later he changed his mind and ploughed it out himself, but what you never had in this life you never miss!

Having had a reduction of 43 acres in the farm, it was now time to look for an increase in acreage. With almost zero rate of land to let in the area, the only alternative was to purchase land. A 24-acre field within easy reach of the farm came for sale. It was part of the Sledmere Estate and was for sale by public auction. We purchased it for £57,000.

If anyone had told us when we moved onto the Yorkshire Wolds in 1959, we should own part of this estate, we would have thought them mad. Two years later another 52 acres, which also previously belonged the same estate, was on the market and we bought this by private treaty at £2,300 per acre.

This gave us 76 acres of our own land and, looking back, it was quite a good investment. Drainage, clearing and ploughing out the old pasture to bring it into the arable rotation would have been very expensive, so money saved there went to help towards the purchase of our own land. Not only that, we now had more land and of better quality than the land we had terminated.

Our total acreage was now 372 acres and our cropping was ware potatoes and oil seed rape for break crops and first and second wheats only for our white crops. All the wheats and oil seed rape were grown on contract for seed, so we were unable to go into the production of seed potatoes.

At this point of time, June, 1986, a ten-acre adjoining field came for sale by auction. I was unable to attend the sale as were away on holiday at the time. So my son-in-law agreed he would go on my behalf. The maximum we would pay was £20,000 or £2,000 per acre.

Already owning land in the village, it was in our interest land should not be sold cheap or, if it was going to be cheap, we'd better be the owners. To my astonishment the price we paid was £19,500 and, further to that, the runner-up happened to be our landlord!

115

With the acreage gradually increasing and specialisation put into place, it made it possible to maximise profits both from crops and livestock and also use what we thought was the most suitable system to farm this unit. The on-floor drying capacity had to be increased, taking the total storage for grain including the ten drying bins to 1,000 tons being dried at any one time, albeit rather slow.

I have never ever used a through dryer as it always seemed to me the greatest problem with grain was finding somewhere to put it. Placed on a ventilated floor, where warm or cold air could be circulated through it at any time, gave one full control at all times. Grain never went wrong with air flowing through it.

This was one of the cheapest ways to dry corn; it also cut down on movement of grain and enabled the operator to go to bed and sleep sound every night.

The 1980s proved to be one of the most prosperous decades for cereal production in my farming career — the increase in yields that technology had brought, plus the price of grain, which had been higher than anyone could have predicted. Together with the favourable weather in the area, both for the growing crop and the harvesting of it, all helped to achieve this.

Pigs as usual had their ups and downs but, on the whole, contributed to the output of the farm until a depression came in the late Eighties, making the pig unit a non-paying enterprise. Mother Nature once again stepped in, reminding me I'd got to the age when I no longer needed a challenge, so the pigs were sold. The farm then became all arable; the only animal left was the old sheepdog, who had never seen a sheep in her whole life!

After 20 years in cows Geoff and I decided to dissolve the partnership, which in many ways, was a sad day for both of us. We had never had a wrong word or any dispute for that matter over all those years. However, it did end on a high note — with an excellent sale of the pedigree Friesian cows with a herd average of £1,700 each, which was a high price for cows even at the time.

The only partnership left now was with my wife Marian and I'd often told her it was a wonder I hadn't traded her in for a young blonde after 20 years. Her reply was "You wouldn't have known what to do with her?" Well, I must say I have been learning all my life and if there has ever been a problem, my motto has always been: 'If at first you don't succeed try, try again'.

On 25th April, 1987 Philip, our second grandson, was born to Charlie and Gwen — yet another grandson. It seemed to Marian and myself that the new generation had dramatically changed sex. We had always been used to little girls running about — it was quite a novelty to see little children playing with tractors and boyish toys instead of prams and dolls!

Being tenant farmers and not owning a house, it had always been our ambition to build a retirement home to our own specification. This we now decided to do and still keep the farm on, as there were significant tax advantages and it was prudent to have it paid for before retirement day. It also gave Marian security if anything untoward happened to me.

Bankers and accountants maintained that 85% of tenant farmers in this country at retirement age have not enough capital to finance their retirement home. So much for the general public opinion that all farmers belong to a wealthy race.

We started looking for a building plot in an area we thought would be suitable. Having lived nearly 40 years with our nearest neighbours a mile away, one had to consider being a little closer to the general facilities of life, taking into account the age we had now reached. We heard of a good building plot at Hornsea, on a small estate boarding the local recreation field, which meant there would always be one open side looking out into the country. It had planning permission for a good-sized house and garden, which looked ideal for our purpose. After all, I had lived the first 32 years of my life with Hornsea the nearest town to home. I had cycled here to both dances and cinema and had played cricket and football on the recreation field: you could say it was almost like going back home.

We bought the plot and decided to build a four-bedroomed house. Marian required all the ground floor to accommodate the furniture we had acquired over our lifetime, but only needed two bedrooms. It is difficult to build a house that shape so, having wanted a snooker room all my life, we decided to leave two of the bedrooms as one, which just happened to be the right measurement to take a full-sized snooker table, once again, killing two birds with one stone.

Having enjoyed the experience of building our ideal home and learnt many lessons for the future, there were two very happy people whose dreams had become true. Having completed the house we stayed there eight nights over the five years we owned it.

Valentine's Day, 1990, saw our youngest daughter Caroline married to Tim Lansdell. April of that year marked yet another milestone, our Ruby Wedding, and the following April with the birth of our grand-daughter, Emily.

Farming was still our life. August, 1991, and yet another field belonging to the Sledmere estate was advertised for sale. It was just over 17 acres and vacant possession was immediately after the wheat crop had been harvested.

It was only a mile away from our own land but was surrounded with land owned by the Crown Estates. The land they owned in this area was over 2,000 acres which was all tenanted land and had recently been bought from the Sledmere Estate.

Death duties had been the reason for the demise of many estates in England, reducing the acreage of land to let to the detriment of young men interested in farming. These estates in many cases had small farms, in the region of 120 to 150 acres, which they let to young men starting up in farming.

If they made a success and looked like making good farmers they would grade them up on to their larger farms, which would be about

118

500-acre units. So this, along with economics, closed the door to many a young man who would have entered farming.

The agent for the Crown Estates had got the idea there was very little interest in the field, as their tenants were in a catch nine situation and very unlikely to be buyers of this land. I had not decided whether to go to the sale or not, as I thought I should be wasting my time, as the Crown would be certain to buy the field in this situation.

The agent who was selling the land advised me the night before the sale to be sure and attend, as he had seen many times before in his life the big boys, who thought there was no opposition, slip up and get it wrong on the day, when they expected to be the certain buyers. He knew I didn't want land sold cheap in this area, nor did he for that matter.

The next day I went to the sale a little apprehensive with tongue in cheek and perched myself on the front row in the saleroom, feeling sure that I would only be a spectator. I was astounded when it was withdrawn from the sale at £32,000 and I was the last bidder!

The auctioneer then made the following announcement: "Would the last bidder meet me in my office after the remaining auction is completed." I duly waited for about an hour, still not believing the position I found myself in.

When he finally summoned me into his office he asked if I was prepared to increase my offer. I then offered him another £500 and made it clear that was my limit.

The agent who was in charge on behalf of the Sledmere Estate was unable to accept the offer, but suggested the auctioneer should contact the owner who was in London to see if he was prepared to accept the price. The news was good for me: he said he would accept, so I put a 10% deposit down and clinched the deal. This took the total acreage we would now farm to 400 acres.

To say I was elated was an understatement. On the way home I decided to tell Marian the land had been far too expensive for my purse. She said that she would not buy that one; she knew by the look on my face that I had bought the field.

Although we were in the midst of harvest, it had got to be half past six and these sort of events don't happen every day of one's life, so we would go out for a meal and celebrate a successful day.

On returning home at ten o'clock, the telephone was ringing. It was the auctioneer enquiring if I would take a profit on the land, as the Crown Estates, who were the runners up, were prepared to negotiate terms for the field.

I said: "I'll take a profit, but the sort of figure I have in mind would be more than they would be prepared to pay, so it'll be better not to waste their time and mine as well." One can only assume their agent thought the auctioneer had not got a bid and he would be able to agree terms later. So their loss was my gain or, as the Governor would have said: "Well bought, half sold."

Buying land was always a gamble, for over the years there had been the odd blip when we all thought the promised serious depression our fathers had predicted was about to become a reality. However, in 1992 the farming boat did start to rock a little: this became the nearest to a depression my generation had ever seen.

Even so it did not affect every section of the farming community. There was always one commodity or one area of the country to escape such a set-back. For instance, taking the meat industry of beef, pork and lamb, even in a year such as this there would be one of these which would still be a fair trade.

As with the potato crop it would very often come up trumps in a poor cereal year. So as the saying goes: 'One man's meat is another man's poison'. During the next two years farming became more stable with price rises in all commodities.

Chapter Fifteen

1995 turned out to be one of the most extraordinary years in our lives — a year when many serious decisions were going to be made. It started when I picked the local paper up one Saturday morning and there before my very eyes was what I had called my dream bungalow for the last 15 years, advertised for sale by a local land agent.

I could not believe what I was seeing and was so excited at the prospect of having the chance to buy it. I didn't mention it to Marian, but jumped straight in the old van, without a thought about the clothes I was wearing and made a bee-line down to town.

Arriving at the agent's office, I walked in and asked the very attractive young lady sitting behind the desk for particulars of Brendon Gates bungalow which they had for sale. She looked me up and down then pronounced: "It is an up-market property, sir." With a smile on my face I replied: "I'm looking for an up-market property, honey."

By this time she realised she had put her foot right in it and caused herself a little embarrassment, and with cheeks glowing red, she handed me the brochure and all the details. On returning home to tell Marian our dream bungalow was now for sale and I had brought the details, she was delighted.

Brendon Gates was built of stone and stood in an acre of gardens, with a six-acre paddock to the south and a small range of out-buildings. I then told her the tale of the reaction of the young lady to my looks. She said: "There's no wonder what the poor girl said, because I would have passed you for a gypsy. How dare you go down town looking like that?"

I then realised how untidy I was and should have changed into smarter attire. What the young lady said may have offended some clients, but I thought it was a huge joke and very often laugh when I think about it to this day. We duly made an appointment with the agent to look round the property the following week.

He opened the front door into the entrance and led the way. I followed and a little voice behind me, said in a whisper: "I could live here." Within two weeks we had bought it.

We now had two dwellings on our books as well as the tenanted farmhouse that we were still living in and, to add to that, a rather large overdraft at the bank as well.

Many times in my life I had been asked advice when buying a new home and moving — should one first sell your existing home or buy your new home?

I advised sell your own home first and get hold of the money, before purchasing your new home. Yet when the time came, Marian and I did the exact opposite and the reason was simple: the ideal home we had set our hearts on was there to be bought. This was a chance in a lifetime — one we were not prepared to miss — so it was 'strike while the iron's hot', or someone else might beat us to it.

We had already realised, before all this, that the house we had built at Hornsea had by now become a non-starter. It was the right house in the wrong place, which is a very important consideration when it comes to retiring and we would never have gone to live there.

The reasons were that, firstly, over the previous five years, there had been tremendous changes. What had been a small quiet estate had now become much larger with over 200 more houses of variable quality being built on it. Access on and off the estate had not been extended and with a large increase of traffic, one had to queue on a regular basis.

The property, over that time had also been broken into and burgled twice, which did not give one much confidence. This now meant that it was time for the sale sign to go up. We were fortunate to get it sold within three months and made a small profit.

Having bought the bungalow which had a good open south-facing view and was surrounded with mature trees on the other three sides, we realised at the Hornsea property we would never, in our lifetime, have had one mature tree in the garden.

These were the type of things we had been used to all our lives, but had not appreciated until a situation like this had arisen, which makes one realise how lucky we had been to live in the country all those years.

1995 brought more dramatic changes. We were looking forward to moving into our retirement home but, like most tenant farmers, our agreement stated clearly that the tenant must reside in the farmhouse at all times. So we had a problem — no, another challenge. However, we changed from farming the land ourselves and introduced a contract farming system.

The main reason for the change was Mother Nature, who was beginning to suggest — no, demand — it was time we both reduced our work load, if we were hoping to hang around in this world a little longer. Although I had maintained throughout my life there was no such thing in business as taking one's foot off the pedal and slowing down, you are either in or out of the job, but once again in life we had to learn to adapt to the present situation.

There was a farming boom, the like of which we had not experienced before and farming booms are noted for not lasting very long. Turning to contract farming enabled us to sell all our farm machinery at the best possible time. There was still plenty of money in the farming world, and people were looking for good second-hand machinery.

I had always kept our tackle updated and in good repair, very often purchasing new machinery on hire purchase when interest rates were at zero. I was told many times that this was bad business, but I was determined to have a good line of machinery to sell on D-Day and looked on that final sale as part of our pension fund!

The biggest wrench of the whole affair was about people — making the two lads I had employed for many years redundant. I called them lads, because I had known them both when they were school lads and that's what they were to me. The two Phil's, were part of the family and both I would describe as rum lads.

Phil Tuplin was of farming stock, but had tragically lost his father and his uncle within three years, through pneumonia. Both were in their thirties and were farming in their own right. Phil was only five years old when he lost his father. This was 1936, the worst possible time to lose contact with farming as it was nearing the end of the great depression when farm stock sales came to very little money. This money invested then did not match inflation over the next 20 years, so there was not enough capital available to enable one to get back into farming, without gambling and borrowing a large amount of money.

I first met Phil when he came to Home Farm as an eleven-year-old in the Forties, to help with harvest. He was driving a tractor then; much better than the old hands who were still trying to convert from driving horses to tractors. Even at that young age he was capable of ploughing and working land on his own.

Phil came to work for me in 1961 and stayed for 34 years. His starting salary was £11 a week, which was £1.50 above the going rate for agricultural workers at the time.

Phil Woodcock came to me straight from school, so you could say he was home trained. He did have a year's break to attend Bishop Burton Agricultural College and then came back to work with us. As a young teenager he was an excellent cricketer and, in my opinion, could have made county level, but seemed to have more interest in farming and amateur football. He worked with us for 27 years; so together the two of them gave over 60 years' service.

I had warned them over the years that it was unlikely I would be around to see them through to retirement, and I always got the appropriate reply. I was fortunate once again to have had two young men of this calibre to have worked with me over all those years.

One had the ability to have farmed land on his own and the other to have become a professional cricketer, but they both decided on a different way of life and happiness is the criteria in this world and stress the major killer.

To their credit, they moved on in their lives and both found good jobs immediately; in fact, starting the following week. This was in an area where unemployment was very high and the farming community was looking for shedding labour rather than increasing it. So with a redundancy payout and a job equal to the one they left, it was a good business move and very pleasing for me.

With land prices in the area reaching between £3,000 and £4,000 per acre, not only was it the right time to sell the farm machinery, it also seemed the right time to sell the land.

Financial advisers had always told me it was never wrong to take a profit, so 95 acres were sold by private treaty, without even doing any advertising. This left only ten acres, plus the six-acre paddock with the bungalow in our ownership, so I became a tenant farmer only for the few remaining years of my farming life.

The next important step was to keep the tenancy of the farm in hand and, at the same time, live in our retirement home. The first idea that came to mind was to use our bungalow as a weekend holiday home. Weekend holiday homes are fine in the middle of summer, but not so attractive when the snow flakes are flying in the winter months, so that one was soon crossed off the list.

The second idea we considered was to keep an office, a kitchen and a bedroom furnished on the farm and spend the odd night sleeping there. Up to that time the law was not very clear on how many nights one had to reside on the farm to qualify for 'living on the farm at all times'. No one yet had determined how much time was allowed before the tenancy agreement of living on the farm at all times had been broken.

Once again this idea was quashed, as we did not want any expensive court cases coming our way. Finally I decided to approach the landlord and put my cards on the table. To my surprise he had no objection to us keeping the farm on another four years whilst allowing us to go and live in our new home. I came to the conclusion he did not want the farm to become vacant at this particular time.

However, there was one provision. This was that we forfeited our present tenancy agreement and changed it to the new tenancy agreement. This must have been one of the first to be formed, as it had only just become law when we started to negotiate terms. This was much more flexible than the one my brother and I had signed in 1959.

Most of the terms in that agreement went back into the late 1800s and had never been updated over all those years. Many of the statements were still written in, even though they had been revoked by law in the 1947 Agricultural Act. It was no easy task to come to terms on many different points to suit both parties and, to add to that, our valuers and solicitors were not accustomed to many of the finer points which had to be sorted out.

There had to be a change in the date to terminate the existing tenancy from the 6th April back to the 6th October, as this one stated the incoming farmer could not plough land till the 4th November. The new agreement was to do away with following crops, so this meant the incoming farmer would have been at least a month late sowing his winter wheat. This would have resulted in lower yields, so changing the dates gave both parties an advantage; one got higher yields and the other a reduction in half a year's rent.

This was only one of the many changes that had to be made. Having got an agreement on all the relevant points the new tenancy started on the 6th October, 1995, and will end on the 6th October, 1999.

With all the machinery gone, no labour on the farm and most of the land we had owned sold, we now had 282 acres rented and ten acres of arable which we owned, making our total holding 292 acres to be farmed on contract. The contractor had a fixed charge for the complete job of working the farm, with a percentage bonus on final output.

Although I'd always believed in timelines — which meant a window of about seven days to do most of the essential jobs, to achieve maximum output at minimum costs and to sell the produce at the highest possible price — and this was the only way to be successful and that there was no other way, I was proved wrong.

With the contractor working the land, very often under pressure, that window in many cases became extended through no-one's fault, so lower outputs than we had been achieving had to be accepted. But on the other side of the coin we had also reduced our costs. We had got rid of two major items — machinery depreciation and labour costs.

Not only was there an advantage from not owning machinery, there was the advantage from the sale to invest, making money and not depreciating. The labour charge was now down to zero, no national insurance, no holiday pay, no overtime. All this added together reduced our costs considerably and enabled us to make higher profit than on the previous system, which I was sure could not be bettered.

This must point to the fact that farms below 1,000 acres will either have to turn to contract farming or join forces with others to justify mechanisation. Costings must be kept to point the way forward and to stay in business.

This situation is not about to take place, it is already here; and the

127

advantage of efficient costings at all times keeps one in touch and ensures that every enterprise in the business is paying. This allows you to determine the right time to change directions or even close the business down if necessary.

Having said that, there are certain areas on every farm where it is not possible to move in and out of major enterprises.

For instance, on the hills you must have livestock of one form or another and on arable farms, crop rotations must be followed or you just could not stay in farming.

The harvests of 1994 and 1995 were the best two harvest in my farming career, I thought all my Christmases had come together. You could say it was a stroke of luck to be easing out of farming at this particular time but, as I have said to many a lucky person: 'You make your own luck in this life' — or, as my bank manager always says, 'he likes lucky farmers'.

The following year was about an average harvest and then in 1997 the depression set in, the likes of which my age group had never seen before. Most commodities dropped to half price. This was the first time since 1922 that this had happened and that depression lasted 15 years until 1937 when war was imminent and food was the major priority.

Over the years, history has proved that many a war has been won by starvation rather than fighting the enemy. One would assume the politicians would take this on board, but it never enters their heads in times of plenty.

The only difference between a shortage and a glut is about 1%, and to keep the food requirements of a country within this narrow margin, with nature being what it is, makes the job impossible. So the best policy must always be to have 1% plus in storage at all times and be ready for unforeseen circumstances, particularly when a third of the world is short of food.   ❏

Summary

I COUNT myself as part of the most fortunate generation in farming ever — to have farmed British soil in my own right for over 50 years, plus eight years' experience on home farm under the guidance of my father.

I was told many times in my life that I could not have had a better tutor or master as he always called a spade a spade and common sense featured high in his thinking. He used to say there was no need for work study: 'Just use your head to save your legs' and 'Always go the shortest way to work and the sharpest way when you get there'.

I have ploughed with horses and then seen men land on the Moon, something we had laughed about when reading comics in our childhood days. The introduction of televisions, computers and the Internet and much more technology in every sphere proved almost beyond what the human brain could comprehend.

Once again, as it has done many times before in this world, history repeated itself: farming became a young man's game. The older ones, myself included, just could not keep pace with this sort of progress and as the old stagers in the football world would say: 'It was time to hang your boots up' and become an adviser — but only when asked, as unwanted advice is rarely accepted! In my opinion the most important things to be a successful farmer are: timeliness, accurate costings, man management and a good business sense.

And now as I sit in the sun lounge of my dream bungalow, watching my son-in-law's four shire mares grazing in the paddock, I remember the horses I walked behind many years ago ploughing and working the fields and, for that matter, doing every moving job on the farm.

The grandchildren playing on the lawn, with the paddock lying beyond makes me think of a song from the Sixties which went . . . 'This is the evening of the day; I sit and watch the children play'.

Which leads me on . . . 'The sand castle the father builds for his son on the beach is great, but the one that the child builds by himself is the one which he is proud of and the one that he will remember'.

This is true in later life. To walk into your father's castle, already built, is not the same as building it yourself and it will never give you the same pride, joy and satisfaction as a business created by one's self.

Whilst sitting in my car one day in town, waiting for Marian doing some shopping, a teenaged lad passed by, accompanying a young lady.

He shouted to me: "Give us a fiver mister; you've got a nice car."

My reply was: "If I could change shoes with you, I'd give you this car and all my worldly goods as well."

But I'm afraid this life is like a game of cricket; once the umpire has raised his finger and given you out, it's a road of no return.

Norman Eric Kirkwood died on the 22nd February, 1999.

Family Thoughts

FEBRUARY 22nd left our family with wonderful memories. For me 49 years of a perfect marriage, for the girls and the grandchildren of a wise and loving Father and Grandad. Added to that was his own true story of a lifetime in farming.

Marian.

OVER the years Dad established a 'weekend ritual'.

On Saturday afternoon he went to watch Hull City AFC . . . supporting them in their 'glory years' and more recently through many a relegation battle. His passion for football has rubbed off and remains with the whole family.

Then on Sunday he regularly attended the morning service at Garton Church. For many years he took us all to Evensong, although as time passed by Sunday mornings proved somewhat less appealing to the female members of his household.

To say that he boosted the numbers at both venues would be an understatement.

Dad was always adamant that even if Hull City were to play in a Sunday match at Wembley Stadium, he wouldn't go. The odds of having to abide by this statement, were certainly on his side, as the chances of 'The Tigers' getting there, still seems pretty remote!

Gwen and Caroline.

THE GOOD OLD DAYS

I've often heard my father say, with pride and sometimes doubt,
'The Good Old Days have long since gone. Just what were they
    about?'
To try to solve the mystery and make his statement clearer,
I delved back into history, to quite a different era.
If records of those bygone days, are going to be of good,
It seems there is a language, that must be understood.
Born and bred a country boy. So 'down to earth' was Dad.
'One man a man, two men half and three men only lad'.
At school he was no scholar, he found all his lessons hard.
He dreamed of being a farmer, with his own cows in his yard.
There was a gruelling time ahead, his father governed all,
To Dad it felt like banging his head . . . against a red brick wall.
Wake up, get up, work, eat and drink, was the order of each day.
A motto: 'You're not paid to think' his father used to say.
Week in, week out work never ceased, come wind or rain or snow.
'The harder one works the softer one's bed' was a phrase he came
    to know.
'What you never have you never miss' was a saying quite true.
Dad's teenage years slipped on by and he did what a man had to
    do.
'Jack of all trades, master of none.' It was food for work. No pay.
Quick was the word and sharp were the actions but 'Rome wasn't
    built in a day'.
The days seemed long and evenings short, outings were by the way.
'Joyful evenings brought sorrowful mornings' the Governor used to
    say.
At last a farm came up for sale. A chance for Dad to settle,
He took a wife and realised now, it had to be 'muck or nettles'.
Perhaps in time he will recall his youthful years well spent,
He'll look back on the 'Good Old Days', as maybe heaven sent.

BY CHRISTINE,
Christmas, 1998.

NORMAN was invited to speak at lots of weddings and anniversaries. Many will remember these words:

'Never stop courting as long as you live'.
'Don't just give and take; always give a little more than you take'.
'Do everything together except one thing; don't get cross'.
'When you go to bed at night always sort your problems out before you go to sleep'.

Then, in years to come, you will look back and think that the advice that old kid gave us on our wedding day has proved right.